Hotlife

Isn't it time you got yours?

FIT for FUN

Wealth Creation & Career
Intimacy & Relationships
Empowerment & Confidence
Wellbeing, Health & Fitness

PAUL McQUEEN

Graystone LA Ltd.
Tanner Business Centre
Chew Valley Road
Oldham OL3 7NH
United Kingdom

www.Hotlifestyle.info

Second Edition

Medical Disclaimer: This book is not intended as a substitute for medical advice from a physician. It contains information that is intended to help readers be better informed consumers of health products and activities. Any use of this information is at your own risk. Before beginning any new physical activity or changing calorie intake, it is recommended that you seek medical advice from your doctor. The information provided in this book is for general informational purposes only.

WHAT OTHERS ARE SAYING

"In today's high-octane, high-pressure world, Paul's new book is like a welcome island in turbulent seas. Everyone loves a self-help book. But we often rush our fences in trying to make every change at once. Paul guides us through making sustainable and effective steps towards a more enjoyable life on every level. Highly recommended."
Claire Meadows - Editor in Chief, After Nyne Magazine, and former Huffington Post blogger

„From managing stress and anxiety to the art of good communication, finding your true vocation and improving sexual intimacy, McQueen writes with great insight and relevance - supported by highly effective techniques, exercises and personal challenges that will help create positive and lasting changes to our health, wealth, relationships and much more."
Martin Gill - Assistant Editor, Yoga Magazine

"Paul McQueen has written the ultimate self-help book. Comprehensive and accessible, Hotlifestyle is a lifestyle, not a book. It covers all aspects of life with great summaries of each chapter. This brilliant book gives you the tools to make great choices and live your best life. Life-changing stuff."
Catherine Balavage - Editor, Founder and Publisher, Frost Magazine

GET THE MOST OUT OF THIS BOOK

Living a Hotlifestyle requires an effective routine and making the right choices to positively impact your life. In your enthusiasm to get cracking you might be tempted to read this book from cover to cover without acting on it. Take your time, it's not a race. Enjoy the journey on the road to success.

Start at the beginning and read chronologically because it really is four books in one, focusing on four key areas to lift you out of a cycle of failure. Each section naturally leads to the next and every chapter conveys the latest evidence-based findings, written in a concise, no nonsense format.

Read each chapter through so you understand the bigger picture. Go back and work on the parts you think will benefit you the most. Finish each section before going on to the next. You might not need to take any action from some chapters. Read them anyway, remember, knowledge is power. Exclusive to this book are links to hotlifestyle.info that take you deeper into the subject matter.

The level of success you achieve comes down to the choices you make after reading this book. What you choose to focus on during the next few months will decide what you will be doing during the next few years.

Are you ready to get your life on track?

16 THINGS YOU CAN ACHIEVE WITH THIS BOOK

1. Use a proven method to create wealth and deal with debt

2. Find your vocation and improve your earnings potential

3. More confidence and success with job interviews

4. Enjoy more sex and intimacy with your partner

5. Understand sexuality and the needs of the opposite sex

6. Deal with setbacks and failures, turn them to your advantage

7. Gain friends by mastering rapport using non-verbal cues

8. Choose the right self-defence system that best suits you

9. Improve your memory with easy to learn techniques

10. Learn how to help others remember things you say to them

11. Deal better with anxiety, stress, back pain, and emotions

12. Make the best first impression on everyone you meet

13. Make bold decisions in your life with unstoppable confidence

14. Get a restful night's sleep and not wake up feeling groggy

15. Develop healthier habits and get fit in 20-second blocks

16. Greatly improve the overall quality of your life and wellbeing

Hotlifestyle
Get Smart with Money

The Best Handbook Dealing with Personal Finances

Practical, actionable tips to help you get out of debt. Form good financial habits to keep a grasp on your hard-earned cash and start working towards financial independence. Includes free money planners.

www.Hotlifestyle.info/cash

Hotlifestyle
Dear Bully, You're Fired!

Get rid of your bully, once and for all.

With a pull no punches approach Paul McQueen takes you on a journey of realization offering real answers showing you a step by step plan to getting your bully fired. You decide whether to play softball or hardball with the bully. He will help you align your emotions to cope with the darn awful situation you find yourself in changing your whole way of thinking. www.Hotlifestyle.info/bully

COVERING THE BASICS

VITALITY

1. Weight Management   21
2. Standing Tall   41
3. Sleep Strategies   57
4. Anxiety   81
5. Wellbeing   97

LIFESKILLS

6. Appearance   113
7. Stress and Emotions   131
8. Empowerment   145
9. Memory   161
10. Self-Defence   177

INTERACTIONS

11. Communication   189
12. People Skills   207
13. Body Language   225
14. Intimacy   239
15. Sexuality   247

ENTERPRISE

16. Career   263
17. Wealth Creation   273
Epilogue   285
Contributors   287

You are what you think you are ...

~ Paul McQueen

PREFACE

Welcome to Your Life. How's It Been So Far?

Imagine how different your life would be, if you chose to live every day to your fullest potential. Take a moment to answer spontaneously: what are your three most important goals? Three things that, if you made them happen this year, would make your life truly amazing. You could make a note of them and look back at them in a year.

1. _____

2. _____

3. _____

How close are you to achieving any of those things you want in life? Are you even setting goals? Do you find yourself so caught up in your daily problems, that you end up neglecting relationships, career, and health? Have you lost track of who you are and why you're here?

It's time to switch off the TV, throw out the junk food, and get what you know you deserve. You know you want more out of life and that you have the willpower to achieve it. Discover the routines successful people use that make a difference to their lives; lay down the foundations so that you too can develop your full potential and enjoy life to the full. I want you to become the very best version of yourself that you can be and enjoy every moment of every day.

Time, or rather a lack of it, is cited as the main reason for not achieving. The week starts and, before we know it, it's the weekend again. When it comes to reaching your fullest potential every day, it has a lot to do with routine, time management, keeping a positive approach and persistence.

THE BOTTOM LINE

Your life is what you make of it, no one else is going to do it for you. If you don't have control over your own life, then it's like watching television without having control of the remote. Someone else is pushing the buttons.

So, if you're ready to take control and personal responsibility to improve your life, I invite you to take the first steps toward your Hotlifestyle. You'll be making the best investment ever - that is, investing in yourself.

There has been real progress in recent years in understanding the concept of a healthy, happy, more fulfilling life, and how to live it. If you are one of the few who naturally have a positive outlook on life, go regularly to the gym, have a great circle of friends, and have found your soulmate, then consider yourself lucky. The rest of us are going to have to work at it on a day by day basis. Yes, living a Hotlifestyle takes some work, but it may be the most rewarding and fun work you will ever do.

Surely Living a Hotlifestyle Is Only a Question of Money?

Believe it or not, becoming a millionaire will not make you happier (OK, a little happier - but only in the short term). There's a statistic that deems those who earn around £70,000 a year are quite happy. Earning more than this does not increase happiness. Let me give you an example. If I simply gave you a million pounds, what would happen? First, your current circle of friends will view you very differently, and you will be asking yourself if they are only with you for what they can get out of you. Millionaires are constantly asking who they can really trust. On the other hand, the "Ascot" crowd won't accept you either, wrong accent, wrong school, and so on. Managing large amounts of money is not as easy as you think. This phenomenon has been well documented in lottery winners who, for the most part, end up alcoholic, lonely, and depressed. I'm not saying that money isn't important, it's just not the single deciding factor leading to happiness, it's just part of the mix leading to a Hotlifestyle.

Unless you have chosen to venture across the Gobi Desert, live in a tent or take a year out to hike across South America, then you probably think that true happiness is really only a question of money. Realizing that a Hotlifestyle is relative to your current standpoint or status in life is the first step to a deeper understanding of what can make you happy. If you are blind, then being able to see would certainly be considered a step closer to a Hotlifestyle. It's more to do with becoming the best version of yourself one step at a time.

Why is it that the people we think should be enjoying their lives to the maximum and having a really Hotlifestyle abruptly decide to exit this world? The Oscar winning actor Philip Seymour Hoffman surprisingly committed suicide through an overdose of heroin just seven days before completing a major movie. L'Wren Scott, the fashion designer and girlfriend of Mick Jagger, hanged herself with a scarf. The shock for Jagger was such, that he had to cancel concerts. The great film director Tony Scott, famed for Top Gun and True Romance, died after jumping off a bridge into Los Angeles harbour. A week after his mother died world renowned fashion designer Alexander McQueen took a cocktail of prescription drugs, cocaine, and then hanged himself. The much-loved actor Robin Williams cut his wrists and hanged himself while his wife was asleep in the same house.Amy Winehouse, Linkin Park singer Chester Bennington (aged 41), and many more, all wealthy individuals with solid careers decided to leave us far too early.

Without delving into specifics, it could be said that in all cases something was seriously missing in their lives for them to take such drastic action, and it certainly was not a lack of money.

It's our natural ability to adapt, that works in two directions. Because we are so adaptable, we quickly get used to many of the accomplishments we strive for in life, such as landing the big job or getting married. Soon after we reach a milestone, we start to feel that something is missing. We begin wanting yet another worldly possession or eyeing a social advancement. But such an approach keeps us tethered to the hedonic treadmill, where happiness is always just out of reach, one toy or one notch away. It's possible to get off the treadmill entirely by focusing on activities that are dynamic and attention-absorbing, and are thus less likely to bore us than, say, acquiring shiny stuff.

What does lead to a Hotlifestyle is a deep inner happiness and peace within yourself after a job well done, being respected and liked by others, and finding that special someone you can trust and be intimate with.

We are going to take you on a journey of self-discovery. Living a Hotlifestyle is not merely being an observer. It's not „joy" or a „temporary exhilaration", or even satisfying a momentary whim. Someone in pursuit of a Hotlifestyle is living a life which has depth and deliberation; a meaningful life that is utilizing your gifts and time; it is living purposefully.

THE CRUX OF IT

A Hotlifestyle involves a willingness to learn, and stretch, and grow, it requires discipline. Most of all it requires active participation and a desire to become the best person you can be. It's time to start making informed lifestyle choices leading to the best version of yourself for a healthier, happier and richer you.

Enjoying a Hotlifestyle begins with getting essential basic aspects of your life in order. The four key areas you need to power up your life are:

Book 1	**Vitality**
Book 2	**Lifeskills**
Book 3	**Interactions**
Book 4	**Enterprise**

Each book encourages you to consider the choices you make and to practise good long-term habits, keeping an open mind when it comes to change. Most of us are reluctant to make changes, especially when it comes to leaving your comfort zone. Soon after you have taken on board these good habits, let them become an intricate part of your life and you will eventually stop consciously thinking about them.

The aim of this book is to enlighten you and point you in the right direction. You already have your daily routine. I want to help you build on that routine; to harness the power of the butterfly effect, with a series of small changes that can positively impact your entire life.

I want you to look back in six months' time and be proud of how you created such positive change in your life.

Are You Ready to Start This Journey?

Change can be intimidating but, once you embrace it, your world will light up with the immense possibilities you have created.

BOOK ONE

VITALITY

Embracing Healthy Habits

HEALTHY, WEALTHY AND WISE

INTRODUCTION

We should be able to deal with this section in just one sentence. Eat healthy foods, drink lots of water, exercise every day, and get a good night's sleep. Done!

Why is it so difficult to follow this simple advice?

Healthy habits are not generally taught as part of the school curriculum. Especially information about nutrition and fitness, which often comes from our parents. As their education was equally limited and their eating habits came from their parents, the information we are relying on is outdated.

Treating your body with some respect and making healthy lifestyle choices is fundamental to achieving your optimal mental and physical wellbeing. Though many things may contribute to your overall health, studies show that our best defence against disease and degeneration is a nutritious balanced diet and regular physical activity. Cutting down on smoking and your alcohol intake, reducing stress levels, allowing your body to rest each day, and getting enough quality sleep rounds off a really healthy Hotlifestyle.

Remember, prevention is always better than cure. So, learn the healthy habits contained within these pages, and I guarantee that your body will thank you for it in the years to come.

After all, it has to last you a lifetime!

*To keep the body in good health is a duty,
otherwise we shall not be able to keep our mind
strong and clear*

~ Buddha

CHAPTER ONE

Weight Management

Healthy Body, Healthy Mind

Managing your weight is the starting point to living a healthy Hotlifestyle.

Today's fast-paced, consumer-orientated world simply encourages unhealthy lifestyle choices, especially when it comes to food and physical exercise. The statistics speak for themselves. The United States of America has the highest rate of obesity in the world, which means more than 33% of adults are classified as obese. The United Kingdom is not far behind, with around 28% of adults classified as obese. During the past 30 years, obesity has skyrocketed across Western countries. On the other hand, less than 7% of the population of industrialized nations like Japan, India, and China can be considered obese.

I asked Pollyanna Hale, a qualified personal trainer and weight loss coach of long standing, to share her thoughts on the benefits and ways of managing weight.

We should all strive to stay within a healthy weight range because there is much, much more to health than size and weight. Being overweight is associated with many health conditions:

➢ type 2 diabetes

➢ hypertension (high blood pressure)

➢ heart disease

➢ certain types of cancer

➢ strokes

➢ liver disease

Some people have a tendency to store fat around their vital organs, which can suffocate under layers of what is known as intra-abdominal fat. You are more likely to be storing intra-abdominal fat if you have a waist measuring more than 80 cm for a woman or 90 cm for a man. It is more common in people described as apple shaped.

It is important to make a distinction between losing stored body fat and losing weight. Losing muscle mass can be an unwanted side effect of dieting too long and over exercising. It is only the body fat that you want to lose, which you can manage through your choice of food and exercise routine.

To Manage, You Have to Measure

The most widely recognized method for determining a healthy weight is the Body Mass Index (BMI). This is a way of calculating whether your weight is in healthy proportion to your height. The World Health Organization defines 'overweight' and 'obesity' in adults as:

➢ overweight is when you have a BMI <= 25

➢ obesity is when you have a BMI <= 30

➢ and the optimal range is a BMI of 21-23, which is the recommended adult goal

Check your own body mass index:

hotlifestyle.info/bmi

My BMI: _____   Date: _____

Body Fat Percentage

The percentage of fat in your body can be measured using bio-impedance scales, which work by sending a harmless, painless electrical current through your body to measure resistance. These scales are perfectly safe, and your doctor or gym may have a set. A healthy body fat percentage is considered to be between 10% and 20% for men, 20% and 30% for women.

What is Healthy?

Measuring a person's BMI is a useful tool for measuring body weight to height ratios for most people, but it does not indicate a person's overall nutritional health or lifestyle.

Muscle weighs more than fat. A person who is lean and toned will weigh more than a person of exactly the same size who has little muscle tone. If you are exercising while cutting calories you may be gaining muscle as you burn fat. This is a very healthy way of getting fit.

However, it would be easy to get disheartened if the scales aren't saying you've lost much, and you may even gain a small amount of weight at first as you tone up. If this is the case, you'd be better off viewing your achievements by measuring your waist, thighs, buttocks, upper arms or wherever else you want to lose weight from - and take note of how your clothes are getting looser. Getting toned means you'll end up going down a clothes size, glowing with health!

Is your BMI under 19? Being underweight should be taken just as seriously, as it also negatively affects your health. Gain weight with nutritious food and avoid junk foods while you work with a qualified fitness instructor. Eating disorders like anorexia, should only be dealt with by a health professional.

Is your BMI over 25? When you consider the health risks, isn't it reason enough to start working on a diet right now?

Energy Management

The principle of all diets - and I mean ALL diets - is this.
Restrict calorie intake to less than calorie expenditure!

In other words, if you eat more calories than you burn, you put on weight. If you eat less than you burn, you lose weight.

1. Calories are the measurement of energy your body derives from food, per its weight; usually expressed on food packaging as kcal per 100 grams.

2. Calories are the measurement of the amount of energy you expend each day.

Find out what your daily calorie requirements are:

 hotlifestyle.info/CC

Be honest when filling in the form for more accuracy.

Calories needed to maintain your weight: _____ kcal/day

Carbohydrate: _____ grams per day

Fibre: _____ grams per day

Protein: _____ grams per day

Fat: _____ grams per day

Calorie AWARENESS, Not Calorie Counting

There's no need to count calories meticulously, as this system can become time consuming and obsessive. However, you do need a rough knowledge of whether different foods and meals are high, medium, or low in calories, depending on their content and portion size, to be able to cut your calorie intake. A comprehensive list of calories contained in common foods can be found below the calorie calculator on:

 hotlifestyle.info/CC

Tips to Reduce Calories

Sleep longer. A Stanford University study showed that people who had five hours or less sleep a night had 15% more of the hormone ghrelin (which stimulates appetite) and 15% less of the hormone leptin (which lets you know you are full) than people who slept for eight hours. So, sleep more and you'll want to eat less; that's the best weight loss technique I've ever heard of!

Trim visible fat off meat and remember that 'skin' on meat and poultry is very high in fat.

Fill up on vegetables and have small amounts of fattening foods alongside. That way you feel full, don't miss out on foods you love, and don't overeat.

Introduce a Mediterranean diet into your daily routine. It adds variety to your menu and there are hundreds of studies showing a multitude of health benefits for those who follow a Mediterranean diet while enjoying delicious food.

For further reading visit:

 hotlifestyle.info/vit/med

Make your own dressings using vinegars (all types), cold pressed oils, lemon juice, fresh herbs and spices, tabasco sauce, soy sauce, mustard, and mint sauce - and throw out the mayonnaise. Highly flavoured foods, such as garlic and chilli, will perk up dishes, as will small amounts of strongly flavoured ingredients, such as Parmesan cheese and anchovies. There are lots of recipe books on the Mediterranean diet, follow the link above to find out more.

WHAT You Eat Matters, Just as Much as Calories.

There are certain things that can be learned from all that dietary information we are bombarded with - after all, there are genuine reasons why you do lose weight if you follow it. Let's take the elements that make diets work and see how we can incorporate them as part of a lifelong eating plan.

NOTE: If you have a diagnosed medical condition that impacts your weight, consult your doctor and get your health under control before considering changing calorie intake without supervision. If your BMI is over 30 or under 19 then we highly recommend that you seek medical advice from a doctor local to you.

Manage blood sugar levels with foods that have a low glycaemic index (GI) rating, that will fill you up quicker and make you feel fuller for longer.

Your digestive system breaks down carbohydrates (found in grain, potatoes...) into glucose (sugar), which enters the blood and is utilized for energy by the body. Because of this, foods containing carbohydrates (carbs) can raise blood sugar levels more than other nutrients. Don't confuse this with refined sugars, we are talking about the natural process of your body converting carbs into glucose for energy.

Fibre is also a type of carbohydrate found in vegetables, fruits, nuts, beans, and whole grains which is non-digestible, but makes you full and helps prevent constipation.

The glycaemic index (GI) is a recognized ranking of how different carbohydrates (carbs) will raise blood sugar (glucose) levels when eaten. So, eating high-fibre, low GI foods has been shown to reduce your risk of type 2 diabetes and heart disease, significantly lower cholesterol levels, and promote friendly gut bacteria in the process.

Eat fewer grains, potatoes, and sugars - these GPS foods rapidly increase blood glucose levels. High levels of glucose are highly inflammatory.

Find out which foods rate as low (good carbs) on the GI table:

 hotlifestyle.info/GI

Eat a balanced diet. This should be a daily intake of about 60% 'good,' fibre-dense carbs, 25% proteins and 15% healthy unsaturated fats (contained in nuts, seeds, fish, avocado, etc.).

Low calorie, watery, plant-based foods - such as fruit, vegetables, and salads - are bulky, filling and provide key vitamins and minerals.

Fibre fills you up, keeps you full for longer, and can help clean your gut. Great high-fibre foods are: split peas, black beans, kidney beans, chickpeas, lentils, green peas, asparagus, broccoli, Brussels sprouts, cabbage, raspberries, blackberries, avocado, carrots (raw), artichoke hearts, and all kinds of nuts.

Protein suppresses your appetite. Eat sources of protein like meat, poultry, fish, eggs, and dairy in moderation. Consumption of red meat preferably lean shoudn't exceed 17oz (480g) a week and fish 7oz (200g) a week. High protein, vegan-friendly, plant-based foods - such as tofu, lentils, edamame, broccoli, spinach, avocado, Brussels sprouts, beans, nuts, and seeds - should be included in your diet more often.

Fat is high in calories. If you want to eat fatty foods without gaining weight you will have to eat less of them.

Calorie-restricted meals and snacks can help. Look at the labels. Is there a lower calorie option you might enjoy?

Avoid processed foods. Try eating foods close to their original form. Juicing is a far less healthy option than a real piece of fruit. For more reading on protein and fibre go to:

 hotlifestyle.info/FP

Intermittent Fasting

Extensive studies have shown that up to two-thirds of dieters regain more weight than they lost after the diet was set aside. And there is little scientific support for the notion that dieting leads to lasting weight loss. This means that the longer you diet, the fatter you'll become once you stop your diet. This is commonly known as the yo-yo effect. Constant long-term dieting is therefore not the answer to weight management

What is the key to long-term energy management?

The findings of a controlled study (The MATADOR study) of 51 obese men at the Queensland University of Technology, Australia, showed conclusively the benefits of intermittent dieting - also called reverse dieting.

More on the MATADOR study can be found on:

 hotlifestyle.info/vit/mat

HOW You Eat Also Matters

There is an effective approach called intermittent fasting, in which your eating pattern involves regular fasting. The power of intermittent fasting is so far-reaching that many studies have shown it can enhance the ability to burn fat, improve metabolic health, decrease inflammation, allow gut bacteria to regenerate - and may even help you live longer.

Fasting has been around a long time, either involuntarily due to shortage of food, or as a religious tradition. You already 'fast' every day while you sleep. Intermittent fasting can be achieved by extending this natural fasting period and missing breakfast, taking your first meal at midday and your last meal at 8:00 pm. You have then been fasting for 16 hours and restricting food intake to an eight-hour window.

This is known as time-restricted fasting and is called the 16:8 diet. It's not necessarily about eating less, it is more about restricting the time in which you can eat. During that eight-hour window when you can eat, try to eat normally and don't binge. Hunger pangs can be an issue in the beginning, while your body is adjusting to not eating for extended periods of time. Exercise toward the end of your fasting period can give added benefits (but only if you are up to it).

Once you've tried this method a few times, do it regularly a few days a week or a few days a month.

THE CRUX OF IT

The crux of the 16:8 diet is:

Eat normally during an eight-hour window, say between 12 noon and 8:00 pm.

The 5:2 Diet

The 5:2 diet is an evidence-based method in which you eat normally for five days of the week, then restrict your calories to 500-600 on just two, non-consecutive days of the week. Many people find that following an eating pattern is easier to stick with than a traditional calorie-restricted diet.

A typical routine would be to: 'fast' on Mondays and Thursdays; eat normally on the other days of the week. On the 'fast' days, your calorie intake is limited to 500 (for women) or 600 (for men) low-carbohydrate calories. If you don't overcompensate by eating excessively on the other days, then this method will lead to a reduced calorie intake, which will help you lose weight.

How on earth can I get by on only 500-600 calories in a day?

This may not be as difficult as you think. Meals can be split throughout the day or eaten in one go. We recommend that you plan carefully. Remember 'we are what we eat,' so, for a healthy weight loss, get a variety of nutrients from a variety of food sources, limit your portions, and burn more calories than you eat. Drink plenty of water and teas as they contain no calories. I suggest you split your intake as follows:

➢ breakfast under 100 calories

➢ lunch under 150 calories

➢ dinner under 250 calories

Tips and recipe books of meals with 500 calories on:

 hotlifestyle.info/500Cal

THE CRUX OF IT

The crux of the 5:2 diet is:
Limit calories to 500-600 on two non-consecutive days of the week but eat normally on the other five days.

Promote Friendly Gut Bacteria

Three pounds (1.5 kg) of bacteria live in your gut, helping with a variety of biological tasks, like digesting certain types of fibre. Promoting healthy gut bacteria means feeding the good bacteria with prebiotic, fibre-rich foods, while limiting foods that feed the bad bacteria, which, strangely enough, are GPS foods (Grains, Potatoes and Sugars). Eating lots of fibre if you have unbalanced micro-flora can cause side effects, such as bloating or a reactive bowel function. We don't want you to become an outcast at the yoga club now do we.

To reduce the side effects of eating high-fibre foods, start off with small portions to allow your body to get used to them. Drinking plenty of water also helps but not the fizzy stuff.

Some foods will affect you more than others, so keep a list of those that you tolerate better. After a while your gut will settle down and the symptoms will subside.

Eating high-fibre foods is too important to give up on it too easily. From the list below, you should eat prebiotic at least three times a week and probiotic at least twice a week.

Prebiotic, fibre-rich foods: barley, oats, apples, all kinds of nuts and seeds, legumes, beans, peas, berries, honey, brewer's yeast, algae (spirulina, chlorella, nostoc).

Prebiotic, inulin-rich foods: chicory root, leeks, onions, garlic, Jerusalem artichoke, asparagus, bananas.

Probiotic, fermented foods that are kept refrigerated: natural live bio-yogurt, cultured cottage cheese, feta, sauerkraut, miso, kombucha tea, kvass, olives in brine, sour pickles.

Probiotic supplements for those who can't stomach fermented foods on a regular basis. Choose one with several different strains of bacteria, including at least: L. acidophilus, B. longum, B. bifidum, L. rhamnosus, L. fermentum. Store them in the fridge. Best taken half an hour before eating.

To help you understand this important subject more fully visit:

 hotlifestyle.info/vit/flora

Move More, Exercise Less

The UK Department of Health recommends 30 minutes of exercise a day that raises your heart rate slightly, such as brisk walking, dancing, gardening, or climbing stairs. If you're office based, then try to move around at least every 90 minutes.

Resistance exercise, such as lifting weights or body weight exercises, build muscle, while cardio exercise, such as jogging and cycling, work your heart and lungs.

All movement burns calories, even day-to-day activities. Here are some ways to get more movement into your day:

➢ **Work at a standing desk** - put your computer on a raised surface so you're standing, which burns more calories than sitting and is better for your posture.

➢ **Use the stairs** rather than taking the lift wherever possible.

➢ **Carry shopping bags by hand** - make sure you have an even load on each side.

➢ **Get a pedometer app** to keep track of your steps and do at least 10,000 a day - pace while on the phone and do short errands on foot rather than driving.

➢ **Clean the house** and put some effort into it, or do some gardening - you'll get fresh air and top up on vitamin D.

➢ **Set a timer** to go off every 90 minutes to remind you to get up and move - a few squats or push-ups all add up over the day.

High Intensity Interval Training (HIIT)

HIIT is effective cardiovascular training that focuses on short, intense, maximum effort bursts of 15 - 30 seconds followed by a short rest period of 10 - 20 seconds. There is no standard workout, the aim is simply to increase your heart rate. You can do it walking, cycling, swimming, or body weight training. The most commonly used form is the Tabata Method where you train hard for 20 seconds, rest for 10 seconds, repeat eight times.

If you have any doubts about exercising at maximum intensity, or you are new to it, you should consult a health practitioner or qualified fitness trainer before attempting such an intense cardio workout.

A suggested training session can be found on:

 hotlifestyle.info/vit/hiit

The Case for Supplements

Supplements are no substitute for a healthy well-balanced diet. However, for optimal health there are certain supplements that have a good reason to be a part of our busy, stressful, modern lives. There aren't many I would recommend, but the following have been proven to show health benefits when good quality supplements are taken in therapeutic doses.

Omega 3 oils - The benefits of omega-3 oils from fish are well documented. They're anti-inflammatory, increase immunity, help protect our skin and joints, and promote heart health. Oily fish capsules are the best source, but krill oil is a good alternative. Best taken with your lunch.

Powdered Superfoods - A high-quality superfood supplement added to smoothies or yogurt is a great alternative to a multivitamin. These concentrated powders of fruits and vegetables pack a lot of vitamins and minerals into a small dose.

 hotlifestyle.info/vit/SF

Vitamin D - This is important for bone health, skin health, muscle function, immunity, and for normalizing blood pressure. It also helps regulate emotional wellbeing and promotes good sleep. So, especially during the winter months, it makes sense to take this supplement as we get most of our vitamin D from the sun. Best taken with your evening meal as a D3 tablet - if included in a multivitamin then best taken with your breakfast.

B vitamins - A study at Swansea University found people with low amounts of vitamin B1 had difficulty remembering new telephone numbers. Older people have difficulty retaining B12. A B-vitamin complex supplement is highly recommended. Best taken on an empty stomach at least 30 minutes before breakfast.

 hotlifestyle.info/vit/suppl

Let's Sum Up

Being over- or underweight can seriously affect your health.

Use BMI to measure your height to weight ratio.

If you need to lose weight, reduce your calorie intake, but don't diet for long periods - and set realistic goals.

Watch what you eat. Cut back on junk/processed food.

Eat a variety of nutrient-rich foods to get different vitamins and minerals.

Understand the calorie and GI ratings of different foods to manage calorie intake AND blood sugar levels.

Try incorporating a Mediterranean diet into your routine.

Practise regular intermittent fasting, either 16:8 or 5:2.

Drink plenty of water, at least two litres per day.

Help your gut flora by eating prebiotic and probiotic foods.

Start a regular exercise routine. Move more and walk more.

Consider supplementing your diet.

What You Can Achieve

Develop healthier habits for more vitality and success.

Improve the overall quality of your life and wellbeing.

You've got to move it move it

~ King Julien

CHAPTER TWO

Standing Tall

Think Back

If you have ever experienced back pain - and the majority of you will have at some time - then you're in good company. The back is a complicated structure of bones, joints, ligaments, and muscles that can flare up in a protective spasm during the simplest of movements, like picking something up off the floor, resulting in severe pain.

Overuse and abuse of prescription and non-prescription drugs has led many practitioners to reconsider their approach to common conditions such as back pain. Of course, always consult your doctor if your back pain is the result of: a violent injury such as a fall; a previous history of cancer; unexplained weight loss; your walk becoming unsteady; or your spine developing an unusual shape. If your doctor seems unable to pinpoint the cause and is still prescribing painkillers, then ask yourself: Do you worry you'll damage your back if you increase your activity? Do you feel less confident about day-to-day activities? Is your back pain stopping you from doing things you feel passionate about? Are you feeling depressed or anxious about how it's affecting your life?

Are your negative thoughts making your back pain worse?

Recent research has shown that psychological and social factors - such as being unhappy or dissatisfied with your work and the way you perceive your back pain - can make it more likely to develop into a long-term issue.

I spoke to David Rogers - BA(Hons), BSc(Hons), MSc a leading physiotherapist with 20 years' experience who specializes in the biopsychosocial treatment of musculoskeletal pain. The biopsychosocial approach targets back pain using both well-established methods of exercise or manipulation and tools from cognitive behavioural therapy (CBT). David has developed combined physical and psychological rehabilitation programmes for patients with persistent low back pain in line with current clinical guidelines. His team includes a doctor and a pain counsellor. An analysis of 85 patients with persistent back pain, enrolled on a programme developed by David and his team, showed substantial improvements by the end, with 73%

of participants having less or no pain. Nine months later, 92% of those who had benefited from the programme still had no pain. Reason enough to ask David to share his thoughts. The old idea of lying in bed for a few weeks taking painkillers has been thrown out of the window.

Help Yourself Get 'Back to Life'

Back pain affects nearly all of us at some point in our lives and is one of the commonest reasons for consulting a doctor, reaching into the medicine cabinet, or taking time off work. Most of the time it resolves itself within a few days or weeks but sometimes it can persist and prevent us from living an active life. When back pain does persist, it is common for it to vary from day to day, making it difficult for us to maintain a consistent level of physical activity. In turn, this can make you feel low and sets up a cycle of poor function, low confidence, and feelings of helplessness.

Back pain was recorded as the most frequent cause of disability, globally, between 1990 and 2013 and, despite vast amounts of money being spent on treatment, investigation, and research, it continues to pose a huge burden on individuals, health services and societies as a whole. The economic costs to health care systems, industry, and social-welfare support systems are unprecedented. According to recent figures from the Office for National Statistics, almost 31 million days of work were lost in 2013 due to musculoskeletal pain problems, costing the UK economy £14bn a year, with back pain being one of the main causes.

Until very recently we had a very poor understanding of the main factors contributing to back pain disability. For many years it was assumed that problems associated with the back were primarily due to structural abnormalities. Traditional healthcare professional training taught clinicians to look for a variety of structural abnormalities of the back, most commonly arthritic and disc disorders, or for conditions attributed to poor posture or deconditioning. Sometimes, treatments focused on these structural abnormalities worked, but far too frequently back pain sufferers would return to the treatment room, frustrated by a further episode or an inability to solve persistent back pain. Fortunately, a more plausible, scientific, biopsychosocial model has now been developed to help us understand why some people develop persistent back pain disability.

Born out of research from various quarters, the biopsychosocial model allows us to understand a person's experience of their pain in the context of their life, culture, hopes and aspirations, past experiences, thoughts, feelings, and relationships. These factors are inextricably influenced by conscious and subconscious information gained from family, friends, media, and healthcare professionals. This new model offers a framework for a better understanding of what happens biologically when back pain persists, the role that psychological and social factors play in back pain disability, and what can be done to promote recovery. Applying this approach helps you navigate the plethora of information you are faced with when suffering from back pain.

The following key messages can: help you make sense of the back pain experience; promote a meaningful recovery in symptoms and function; and allow you to get back to doing the things in life you enjoy.

> ## Be Aware That MRI Scans Have Limited Value in Diagnosing or Treating Most Back Pain

It can be impossible to diagnose what structure in your back is causing your pain, so it is likely to be diagnosed as 'non-specific', which means it is caused by a number of factors, all closely linked to your pain experience. In most instances, an MRI scan of your back won't help to promote recovery as we now know that many common changes found on MRI scans in people with back pain - including slipped discs, worn or degenerative discs, or trapped nerves - are just as common in those who have never had back pain.

Calm Any Worries You May Have About Damage

When back pain persists, it feels as though something must be seriously damaged, but it rarely is. Sometimes such concerns can lead to fear of movement and avoidance of activities. But worrying about damage, and how it might influence your future, plays a major role in preventing recovery. So, keep in check any negative thoughts about damage to your back and tell yourself that it's safe to get moving. Less than 2% of people with back pain complaints require surgery. If you still need reassurance, seek advice from a healthcare professional.

Gradually Return to Activity

It is common to be fearful of activity when back pain persists, particularly if it hurts. The best approach is to get active at low levels and build up gradually, safe in the knowledge that any ongoing back pain isn't harming you. Start at a level of activity you feel you can repeat every day - we call this a 'baseline level' - and gradually increase it. You may find it helpful to write out a plan to follow. It will feel easier as you repeat the activities over a few days and weeks. If you are a member of a gym talk to one of the instructors about a fitness routine that you could do during the times when you have back pain.

Check Your Thoughts

Research tells us that people who think the worst when they experience a flare-up in back pain take longer to recover. So, if you find thoughts going through your head during a flare-up such as, 'I'll never get over this' or 'how can I ever get back to normal again' try to reframe them as 'I can get over this' or 'this will pass' to focus on recovery. We will discuss more ways to deal with unnecessary worry in chapter 4.

Do Some Breathing Exercises

When back pain persists, it is common for muscles to feel tense and tight. You may experience sudden spasms of pain without reason. These frequent episodes are due to your nervous system being oversensitive, like a volume dial for pain being turned up too high. There are numerous breathing techniques that have been proven to promote relaxation, prevent anxiety and over-excitement. When you are stressed you may have noticed that your breathing will be short and when you are relaxed your breathing will be long. Deliberate slow deep breathing using your abdomen soothes and relaxes the nervous system.

Breathing exercises, such as the 7/11 method described over the page, will calm down the nervous system, and the muscles they supply, relaxing tense muscles and preventing sudden spasms of back pain.

The 7/11 Breathing Method

1. Take in a deep breath, allow the stomach and lower ribcage to expand as you breathe in.

2. Breathe out, control the flow so that it is steady and slow, empty out a little more than normal (both through the nose, if possible).

3. Continue taking deep breaths in and long, slow breaths out. When you have got used to how it feels, count the length of your breaths.

4. Breathe in for a count of 7 and out for a count of 11.

5. Adjust the speed of your counting so that it is comfortable.

6. The important thing is to make sure that the out breath is longer than the in breath. This triggers an automatic relaxation response in your body.

7. Continue this for 5 to 10 minutes, or however long you wish. Focus on the feeling and the sound of your breathing.

8. As you breathe slowly, be aware of where your body is supported and think of allowing your muscles to let go of the weight of your body on to whatever you are resting upon.

Exercise Regularly

The back is designed to move and bend and twist in a variety of ways. Protecting your back from these movements might seem like the logical thing to do. But, continuing to avoid exercise will prevent recovery. It doesn't matter what you do - swimming, cycling, walking the dog, joining a gym class, or yoga are all excellent types of exercise. Just make sure it's something you enjoy doing, so you are more likely to continue it in the long term. It may be helpful to work out a plan each week, scheduling time for this exercise within your day.

Involve Family and Friends in Your Recovery

Those close to you want to do the best for you when you are suffering with back pain. Sometimes they can be over-protective and do everything for you. While this is well intentioned, it can prevent you from trying things out that may promote recovery. Remember, your back likes all types of movement, so tell those close to you that it's safe for you to get going, and encourage them to help you work toward a recovery in function.

Manage the Stressors in Your Life

Ongoing, unresolved distress in your life will wind up your body's stress response system, causing tension in your back muscles, which is likely to cause more frequent flare-ups. Some daily stressors, at home or work, can be difficult to control but, if you can find ways to manage them, you will find that your back will be much less troublesome.

This subject is covered in more detail in the Lifeskills section on Stress and Emotions, chapter 7.

Focus on a Structured Plan to Help You Sleep Better

Refreshing sleep is essential for our general health and wellbeing. It is best to avoid using technology before going to bed, including computers, mobile phones, and television; having a bedtime routine leading up to sleep and calming your mind through 7/11 breathing are simple strategies that make a refreshing sleep more likely. While they may not work immediately, persevere with them each evening. Try to avoid long periods lying down through the day or 'catnapping', even if you're not sleeping soundly at night.

The following section on Sleep Strategies, chapter 3 discusses in some detail how to get a good night's sleep.

Prepare for Some Bumps Along the Road to Recovery

Applying these new rules will certainly make a difference. It is very common to experience some 'blips' or setbacks during recovery, so having a plan for when things go wrong with your back is really helpful. The list below details an emergency plan for when you are having a bad day. Keep it close at hand because when a flare-up happens it can overwhelm you and make it difficult to think straight.

A Useful Plan to Manage a Flare-up

➢ Keep calm

➢ Accept the flare-up has happened

➢ Check that your symptoms are familiar

➢ Check your thoughts

➢ Do some 7/11 breathing

➢ Stretch gently

➢ Modify your activity for a short period of time

➢ Use some medication to help you get going again

➢ Return to normal activity as soon as possible

If your back pain persists for more than a few weeks, then seek help from a health professional. They can often promote your recovery and help you to apply these principles to your daily life.

THE BOTTOM LINE

Back pain is rarely due to serious disease. Keep active, safe in the knowledge that the pain is not a sign of damage, which will help promote recovery and pretty soon you'll notice your confidence in your body returning.

Any activity is good for you when back pain presents, but it's important to start activity at a low level and build it up gradually. Going for a walk, doing some simple stretches, or taking up yoga are great ways to promote recovery.

Infrared for Flare-ups

Infrared rays are a simple, cost-effective way of reducing muscle pain. They can penetrate up to 2" (5 cm) deep into body tissue. The deep warming of muscle increases blood circulation and helps your body deal better with inflammation. It brings vital nutrients to that point needed for healing and there are no known side effects to using it.

A US study of 40 patients, who had chronic low back pain for more than six years, showed conclusively that after seven weekly sessions using an infrared wrap, they had a 50% reduction in pain.

Proteolytic Enzymes for Flare-ups

What would you prefer?
A pain killer or a healing enzyme?

Pain killers can alleviate symptoms quickly but don't actually help heal the body, not to mention their possible side effects. Proteolytic enzymes support the healing process AND reduce the symptoms of inflammation. Their anti-inflammatory properties have been documented in many clinical studies. They have been used in Europe for more than 50 years and are available in supplement form. The best-researched enzymes for healing injuries are bromelain, papain, trypsin, devil's claw, and pancreatin. More on this subject in the section on Wellbeing, chapter 5.

Yoga

Yoga techniques can be an amazing tool in the fight to alleviate back pain. They can strengthen, stretch, and improve blood circulation to your back. The hippy status yoga once had has gone and there's no age barrier to doing it. It's even recognized by the NHS. It's also something that can be done at home. So, move the coffee table, roll out your yoga mat, and embrace a yoga session for a better back.

 hotlifestyle.info/vit/y4b

Preventative Measures

It may well be that you've never experienced back troubles. Strengthening your back with special exercises and avoiding activities that can lead to back injury will help reduce your chances of severe back pain. Measures to consider include:

➢ Maintain a healthy weight and diet

➢ Exercise regularly, stretching before and after

➢ Sleep on your side or on your back

➢ A medium-firm mattress minimizes spine curvature

➢ Lift objects from a squatting position, bend at the knees

➢ Keep heavy objects close to your body and don't twist

➢ Maintain a good posture when walking and sitting

➢ If you have a desk job, avoid sitting or standing for long periods

➢ Wear comfortable, low-heeled shoes, less than 1½" (4 cm) high

➢ If you smoke, then quit, it impairs blood flow

➢ Supplement with magnesium, calcium and vitamin D

Further reading found on:

 hotlifestyle.info/vit/FB

Women are More Likely to Suffer from Back Pain

Cramping of the uterus during your period can cause blood vessels to contract, starving surrounding muscles of oxygen. This can cause an aching feeling in your abdomen. A hot water bottle on the affected area can help, as can a gentle massage.

Back pain is very common for those with very large breasts. Seek advice when choosing a bra, which should have lots of support and shouldn't pull down on the straps, forcing you to lean forward.

Stooping down to deal with kids or picking up toys can be a strain on the back. Watch how you bend down and use the right lifting technique. But really there's no substitute for a strong back. Do exercises to strengthen both abdomen and back.

Let's Sum Up

Make sure there is no critical medical condition for the pain.

Remain active and avoid prolonged inactivity or bed rest.

Use breathing techniques to ease symptoms.

Manage the stressors in your life.

Develop a plan for managing flare-ups.

Consider infrared or proteolytic enzymes.

Prevention is better than cure, so create healthy back habits.

A ruffled mind makes a restless pillow

~ *Charlotte Brontë*

———————

CHAPTER THREE

Sleep Strategies

A Wake-up Call

You certainly don't need me to tell you that we live in a 24/7 society in which sleep deprivation has become the norm. Most of us aren't getting enough, and the all-too common attitude of 'Plenty of time for sleeping when I'm dead' might just bring it closer, death that is.

We are experiencing a sleep crisis. The Centers for Disease Control and Prevention (CDC - US government organization based in Atlanta) declared insufficient sleep as a public health epidemic back in 2011, and the situation has become worse.

In recent research those surveyed said: nearly 75% slept less than seven hours per night; 12% got less than five hours a night; 30% complained of ‚poor sleep' most nights - with the top three reasons as stress and anxiety (45%), partner disturbance (25%), and general noise (20%); while more than one in 10 had an uncomfortable bed.

Scientists agree that the quantity and quality of sleep impacts how we look, determines our mood and performance, and influences practically every facet of our life.

It is time to wake up to the reality that quality sleep is key to our mental and physical wellbeing.

You will sleep for roughly one-third of your life. Sleep in human beings follows a natural pattern called the circadian rhythm. It's a sleep/wake pattern that corresponds to the daylight/darkness cycle.

We also have a natural sleep cycle of about 90 minutes, consisting of five stages.

Maybe you are one of those who sleep less during the week, then try and catch up at the weekend, but getting a good night's sleep might be easier than you think.

Time to put on your pyjamas (we'll talk more about that later too) and curl up with a good book - this one will help.

The Mechanics of Sleep

Sleep is a naturally-occurring, periodic, and recurrent state of unconsciousness which gives the mind and body time to recuperate.

The Rhythm of Life

It's only recently that scientists have been able to fully understand the alternating cycle of sleep and waking, and how it is related to daylight and darkness. If you are to lay down strategies for a better night's sleep, then there are three important natural patterns you need to understand.

Circadian Rhythm

Experiments in the 1700s showed how circadian rhythms worked in plants, causing them to open during the day and close up at night. Humans also have a built-in biological, circadian clock. It's an internal timekeeping device that tells us when to sleep, when to wake, when to eat. It regulates many of our physiological processes over a 24-hour period (circadian comes from the Latin circa, meaning 'around', and dies, meaning 'a day'). There are many examples of circadian rhythms: you will tend to wake up at the same time, whether you've set the alarm or not.

The most important gland that exhibits this rhythmic pattern is the pineal gland (located just above the middle of the brain), which is responsible for secreting the hormone serotonin.

Serotonin acts as a neurotransmitter that influences brain cells related to mood, sexual desire, appetite, sleep, memory, learning, temperature regulation, and some social behaviour. Levels are highest at noon and lowest at midnight, whereas the secretion of the hormone melatonin (derived from the chemical serotonin) is highest at night and stops in the early hours of the morning. Increased levels of melatonin makes a person lethargic. This is why early risers find it difficult to sleep in, as their biological clock has already reacted to the wake-up juice, serotonin.

This subject is so important that researchers studying chronobiology (the biology of time and internal biological clocks) were awarded the 2017 Nobel Prize in Physiology for their discoveries of molecular mechanisms controlling the circadian rhythm.

THE CRUX OF IT

The circadian rhythm is our response to light and dark. Routinely going to sleep and waking up at the same time each day helps achieve quality sleep.

Sleep Cycle

One full sleep cycle refers to a period of about 90 minutes, during which you progress through five stages of sleep, 1, 2, 3, 4 and REM (rapid eye movement). This means that if you sleep continuously for 7½ hours you experience five full sleep cycles that progress cyclically, then begin again with stage 1 about every 90 minutes. After REM sleep, you return to stage 1 of light sleep and begin a new cycle. Each stage can last somewhere between 5 and 15 minutes.

It is recommended that you achieve
five sleep cycles every 24 hours.

Graph by EL Hartmann MD (The functions of sleep) shows how during eight hours of sleep you might drift into the various stages of sleep.

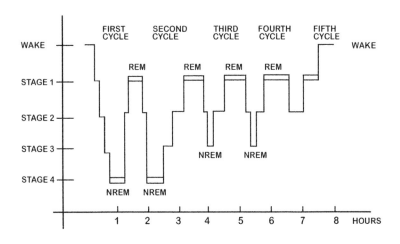

The Five Stages To One Sleep Cycle

Stage 1 (light sleep)

You drift in and out of sleep and can be easily woken. During this stage, you may experience hypnic jerks (sudden muscle contractions) preceded by a sensation of falling. You lose sensory attachment to the physical world toward the end of stage 1.

Stage 2 (light sleep)

Your body temperature begins to drop, and the heart rate slows in preparation for deep sleep. You spend about half your sleep time here in a light dreamless sleep.

Stage 3 (deep sleep)

This is the beginning of deep sleep and another dreamless stage of sleep. It is the period when sleep walking, bed wetting, or talking in your sleep occurs. It's harder to be woken up but should that happen at this stage you will feel especially groggy and confused for a couple of minutes.

Stage 4 (deep sleep)

This is the deepest sleep phase and the most restorative. Not getting enough deep sleep in this phase will leave you feeling groggy in the morning. If roused from this state, you will feel quite disoriented for a while.

REM (REM sleep)

Brain wave activity mimics that of being awake. The eyes move rapidly from side-to-side, hence the name rapid eye movement (REM). It is reckoned that this stage is important for healthy brain function, including the creation of long-term memory. This is the only phase within which you will dream. Should you be woken up during REM phase you can easily slip straight back into this stage when you go back to sleep.

THE CRUX OF IT

View your sleep pattern in blocks of 90-minute sleep cycles. If you sleep for exactly seven hours, you will have woken up in the middle of your fifth sleep cycle, which robs you of your REM phase. It's much healthier to wake up after the cycle is complete and in a light sleep stage.

Chronotype

A person's chronotype identifies their sleep preference in a 24-hour period and indicates their most productive time of day. There are two types: morning (early risers, best in the morning), and evening (night owls, best in the evening). This has practical implications for industry, such as, morning types should be given morning shifts and evening types evening shifts, which is likely to increase their performance.

THE CRUX OF IT

Know which chronotype you are. If you're an early riser you might consider going to bed at, say, 10:00 pm, so five sleep cycles of 90 minutes have you getting up at 5:30 am.

Without enough sleep,
we all become tall two-year-olds

~ JoJo Jensen

Sleep Deprivation

The first documented world record holder for sleep deprivation, stayed awake for over 11 days in 1964. At the age of 16, Randy Gardner from San Diego decided to do a school project to see how long he could stay awake without the use of any drugs or caffeine. By the second day he had problems focusing properly and felt fuzzy-headed; by the third day he became moody and angry with his friends. At this stage he was unable to repeat common tongue twisters like 'Peter piper picked a peck of pickled peppers'. On day four he began to hallucinate and by day five he complained of dizziness and his speech began to slur.

As the days passed, Gardner had problems remembering what he said from one minute to the next and the hallucinations grew worse. After completing 11 days and 20 minutes he then slept for 15 hours and seems to have come out of the experience unscathed. At the time of writing this book he is alive and well.

The current world record was achieved in April 1977 and stands at 449 hours (18.7 days). It is held by Maureen Weston, of Cambridgeshire, England. The category has now been withdrawn due to the inherent risks involved.

Consequences of Sleep Deprivation

The above highlights the short-term consequences of sleep deprivation. Long-term neurological repercussions include loss of motivation, drowsiness, and the inability to make decisions. Studies have also shown that long-term sleep deprivation facilitates weight gain as blood sugar levels can run amok, and it increases blood pressure, depression, and can even cause death. Fatigue, feeling shattered throughout the day, is the most prominent symptom people complain of.

Drowsiness When Driving

Sleep deprivation is a daily road safety concern. Drowsiness can slow reaction time as much as driving when drunk. The National Highway Traffic Safety Administration estimates that fatigue is a cause in 100,000 car crashes and 1,550 crash-related deaths each year in the USA. Also bear in mind, if you stop to take a nap try to sleep for one full cycle of 90 minutes to avoid waking up during stages 3 or 4, which will leave you feeling groggy.

Night and Day Shifts

When your regular routine changes it disrupts your circadian rhythm, which can lead to accidents and injuries at work. In one study, workers who complained of excessive daytime sleepiness were more prone to accidents - and had more sick days.

Jet Lag

Dreading your next long-haul flight? Crossing three or more time zones wreaks havoc with your circadian clock and can result in relentless insomnia, debilitating fatigue, and tormented bowels. There's no way to avoid jet lag, all you can do is alleviate the symptoms by tricking your body clock by planning ahead.

Before You Fly

Travelling west: A few days before travelling go to bed one hour later each night and get up later.

Travelling east: Go to bed one hour earlier each night on the three days leading up to your flight.

During the Flight

Drink plenty of water. Avoid sleeping pills or alcohol, both of which will hinder your adjustment to the new time zone. Being at high altitude multiplies the effect of alcohol on the body and, since alcohol dehydrates, disturbs your sleep patterns even further. Even one glass will worsen your jet lag symptoms. During the flight set your watch to your destination time and try to eat and sleep on the plane as per that time.

Fasting During the Flight

A Harvard Medical School study showed that fasting for at least 16 hours before your arrival can help to override your biological clock. Your digestive system has a lot to do with setting your internal clock. Even if you can't fast, eating as little and as lightly (fresh fruit) as possible can help alleviate some jet lag symptoms.

On Arrival

Travelling west: Get outside in the afternoon sun to help shift your circadian rhythm forward. Recovery time is a little less than one day for each time zone you've crossed.

Travelling east: Get more morning sun to help shift your circadian rhythm backward. Recovery time is a little more than one day for each time zone you've crossed. Travelling east causes more severe, longer lasting symptoms.

No matter how tired you are when you arrive, don't sleep more than one cycle during the day. Better still, try to force a new rhythm by going to bed at your normal time, using local time. Try to read rather than watch television. Eat meals at normal set times and try to avoid eating through the night. Especially on your first day, stop eating at 4:00 pm until breakfast the next day. If your journey is shorter than three days, it is worth trying to keep to your home time during the trip.

Insomnia

Insomnia is a sleep disorder characterised by having trouble falling and staying asleep. Lots of factors can contribute to insomnia, so it's not always obvious what the cause is. It can also be accompanied by another health condition, which is why you should consult a physician if you have periods of insomnia for more than three days.

Only go to bed when you're tired. If you haven't fallen asleep within 30 minutes, get up and do something relaxing, like reading (but not on a screen as LED displays glow with blue light, which suppresses melatonin) until you feel tired enough to try again. Don't clock watch, it will only frustrate you even more about being awake and stop you getting to sleep. It is useful to go through bedtime rituals, as described later.

Yoga is an effective bedtime ritual. Just a few yoga poses prior to going to bed can lead to a blissful night's rest.

Learn some yoga poses for better sleep:

 hotlifestyle.info/vit/y4s

Cognitive behavioural therapy (CBT) and mindfulness can help you deal with any worries that may be causing sleep problems. CBT helps you to understand what healthy sleep is and how to deal with any negative thoughts about sleep.

Promoting a Good Night's Sleep

Sleep is vital to the recuperation of the subconscious mind and is essential for repairing the body's cells and tissues. Experts at the Harvard Medical School looked at MRI scans of volunteers' brains to see which parts are activated after a good night's rest. They found that sleep helps new memories to 'stick' in the brain - a process scientists call memory consolidation. This happens when connections between brain cells are strengthened by proper rest.

You can find more information on:

 hotlifestyle.info/vit/SAM

Sleep also improves learning capabilities, increases your attention span, and aids in decision making. We've all heard the phrase 'let me sleep on it'. Sleeping on a problem can often result in your creative mind finding a solution. Finally, the processes required for growth and to boost the immune system are also intricately involved with sleep.

Bedtime shouldn't just be when you collapse after a hard day's work. It's the start of an important phase that allows your body and mind to recuperate. You should therefore treat your bedtime with proper respect. No one can dictate your perfect bedtime routine, develop one that feels right for you.

Get Regular Exercise

Exercise increases serotonin and dopamine levels, which help to reduce anxiety and depression. However, workouts that last longer than one hour can increase cortisol levels, which is bad.

Avoid Taking Naps

An obvious thing to avoid, however tempting.

Nutrients That Help Promote Sleep

Magnesium - Helps muscles relax and can trigger a calm, 'sleepy' feeling. If you use a supplement in the evening, then magnesium citrate is better absorbed than magnesium oxide.

B vitamins - Taking enough vitamins B3, B5, B6, B9, and B12 improves your sleep. They help regulate levels of the amino acid tryptophan, which helps produce melatonin. Supplement in the mornings, using a vitamin B complex.

Vitamin D - This 'sunshine vitamin' has also been proven to promote sleep. Dietary sources include fish, beef liver, cheese, and eggs. The UK government has advised everyone to take a 10 mcg vitamin D supplement daily.

 hotlifestyle.info/vit/suppl

Getting to Sleep

Get Your Sleeping Environment Right

For half the time in your bedroom you should have your eyes closed - and the rest should be sleeping. That's right, bed is either for sex or sleep!

Make your bedroom a sanctuary - not your office, a TV room or a party room. Create a positive association between your bedroom and sleep by:

➢ making it completely dark, which helps release melatonin

➢ keeping it quiet, with no disruptive beeping of phones

➢ turning your alarm clock so you can't see the time

➢ giving it an optimum room temperature of a cool
16-18 °C (60-65 °F)

➢ using several layers of bedding, so that you can adjust your body temperature if you get too hot or cold

➢ Some suggest sleeping naked

Choosing the right bed is so important that we have further reading on:

 hotlifestyle.info/vit/matt

Cultivate Bedtime Rituals

Stress and anxiety are the main reasons people have difficulty falling asleep, both are covered in some detail later. Try these techniques to prepare a busy mind for sleep:

➢ Try to go to bed at the same time each night - BUT only go to bed when you're feeling sleepy

➢ Use dimmed lights before going to bed in rooms such as kitchen, bathroom and bedroom

➢ Take a relaxing bath about an hour before bedtime - add baking soda and bath salts to warm water

➢ If you opt for a warm shower run it colder at the end

➢ Drink warm milk or camomile tea an hour beforehand

➢ Take a magnesium and lavender supplement

➢ Put a few drops of essential oil of lavender on a tissue and place it under your pillow

➢ Ask your partner for a foot massage

➢ Try the 7/11 breathing method

➢ Keep a pen and paper handy to capture your inspiration

Learn some great methods to help you get to sleep:

 hotlifestyle.info/vit/BM

Things to Avoid

➢ Arguments just before bedtime

➢ Strenuous activity/exercise four hours before going to bed

➢ Caffeine, alcohol or smoking up to six hours before

➢ Phones, tablets and computer screens

➢ Heavy or rich meals late at night

Staying Asleep

Don't be Woken Up by Hunger

If you tend to wake up in the early hours feeling hungry, you could take a light, healthy, low GI snack an hour or two before going to bed. This should not become a regular habit, try to organize your daily eating routine better.

Some light bedtime snack ideas are: 100% whole-grain crackers or bread with a slice of turkey, scrambled egg, banana, kiwi, papaya or half an apple. You could drink tart cherry juice, a camomile or passionflower tea.

If you suffer acid reflux you may consider eating 2-3 hours before going to bed to avoid the symptoms.

Further reading on:

hotlifestyle.info/vit/SR

We can't say this often enough, avoid stimulants after your evening meal. The tea, coffee, or cigarette you have at 7:00 pm is still affecting your body at midnight.

How Alcohol and Marijuana Affect Sleep

Both substances will have you falling asleep quicker, and both promote a deeper sleep in stages 3 and 4 - good news for insomniacs. However, this is offset by increased sleep disturbances in the second half of the night as the effects wear off. Once alcohol has been metabolized, REM sleep is suppressed, and awakenings are common. Alcoholics report having no dreams because of the disruption of REM sleep.

Studies have shown that long-term use of marijuana leaves you wanting to nap during the day, which suggests a lack of quality sleep. Users report more intense dreams for a while after they stop using.

Assume the Right Position

Sleeping on your front is one of the worst positions for your health. The healthiest is the foetal position. Studies say that right-handed people should sleep on their left-hand side, while lefties will be most comfortable sleeping on their right side.

Avoid Getting Up

Don't drink large amounts of fluid up to two hours before bedtime and go to the bathroom just before going to bed.

Disruption

Is your partner a different chronotype? You should have asked THAT question on the first date. Living with a night owl when you're a morning person can cause conflict in the relationship. Someone putting on the light or climbing between the sheets when you're asleep, can really disrupt a cycle.

With a little consideration the night person could get ready for bed at the same time (after all, bedtime is an important time to connect at the end of the day) as you go to bed, leaving a few minutes later then returning as quietly as possible when they are ready for some shuteye. Better still, try to adopt the same sleep schedule.

If one partner moves around more, consider a bigger bed with a memory foam mattress. It's quite common in Europe that a double bed has two separate mattresses which can be adjusted individually.

Not only do men snore more than women, they also tend to be rowdier. Avoiding alcohol and sleeping in the foetal position may be enough to alleviate snoring. Gently rolling someone on their side can help. If snoring is extreme, then seek professional help to be sure there aren't any underlying health issues. Some couples sleep in separate beds/rooms.

Noise pollution is cited as the third most common reason for affecting sleep patterns. Apart from using ear plugs, you can combat noise pollution by playing other background sounds that have a steady soothing effect. It doesn't have to be music, white noise, or the sound of a vacuum cleaner can be just as effective. These noises especially help toddlers go to sleep.

What If You Wake During the Night?

If you really can't get back to sleep, first deal with the disruption (in a nice way). Don't lie there awake, get up and do some small task, like cutting out coupons from magazines. Go through your pre-bedtime rituals and avoid putting on bright lights, which will wake you up all the more.

Waking Up in the Mornings

Create a Post Sleep Routine

After your fantastic night's sleep, the first 90 minutes of the day are the most important to achieving a good start, so having a morning routine can be really beneficial. Waking up at the same time each day is healthy, as we know, so no sleeping in on weekends. A cool room combined with a warm comfy bed can make the decision to get up difficult. Fortunately, technology has moved on when it comes to alarm clocks. There are clocks that will gradually increase the light in the room before playing music, certainly a much more civilized way to break your slumber.

Here is a suggested routine after the clock has gone off.

A Morning Routine

1. While still in bed stretch like a cat.

2. Get up and let plenty of light into the room.

3. Make your bed properly.

4. Some people find taking a daily shower invigorating.

5. Down a full glass of lukewarm water in one go.

6. Have a coffee/tea and breakfast approx. 20 min. later.

7. Set aside at least ten minutes each morning for you.

Start your day with a yoga session:

 hotlifestyle.info/vit/YS

Power up your day with this routine:

 hotlifestyle.info/vit/MR

Let's Sum Up

You will have noticed that we have not suggested sleeping pills, melatonin or 5-HTP supplements, which should be considered only in conjunction with a health practitioner.

Create a great sleeping environment by making a sanctuary dedicated only to sleep - and sex.

Promote a good night's sleep by eating well and exercising enough throughout the day.

Cultivate bedtime rituals that help you wind down from the day and prepare for a good night's sleep. Dim the lights.

Avoid 'blue light' emanating from computers, TVs etc.

What is your natural rhythm? Know when to go to bed and when to wake up.

Have a strategy ready if you wake up through the night and have difficulty getting back to sleep.

Create a motivating morning routine.

What You Can Achieve

A clear mind and improved physical health and safety.

Improved concentration and not being irritable.

Everyone has some anxiety,
but not everyone has anxiety

~ Paul McQueen

CHAPTER FOUR

Anxiety

Being Afraid of Being Afraid

There are times in all our lives when we experience some self-doubt, our confidence may wane a little and we worry. If you're an entrepreneur starting a company, or you're rapidly moving up the success ladder, preparing to speak in public, purchasing a house, or getting married, your thoughts and emotions can be overwhelming as you realize that a game changer is about to take place and you can see all the scenarios that could go wrong. The fear of failure can cause a mild anxiety, whose symptoms are not debilitating so much as irritating.

If this mild anxiety is not dealt with straight away it can lead to further feelings of anxiety and dread, creating a neurological pathway, which can become a habit of anxiety every time you think about the event. By the time you get to the actual event you are so anxious that you are useless.

Anxiety can be triggered when you ask yourself: What might happen? Can I handle it? Do I have what it takes? What if it's not OK? Will it go wrong? Anxiety can also arise from something happening right now that has woken up your fight or flight mode. Make sure your anxiety is not being caused by a lack of skills on your part.

Anxiety can convert into feelings that have physical effects. During an anxiety attack the physical symptoms listed below become the main issue, overriding what caused the anxiety in the first place.

➢ dry or tight throat	➢ shaking or trembling
➢ increased heart rate	➢ sweating
➢ rapid breathing	➢ palpitations
➢ chest pains	➢ pins and needles
➢ hyperventilation	➢ dizziness

In extreme cases the physical symptoms of anxiety can feel like a heart attack. Without doubt it is unpleasant, but it is by no means life threatening. Statistics show that one in three of us will experience anxiety sometime in our lives - and women are twice as likely to suffer with it than men.

This book is for people who want to get more out of life by giving you a competitive advantage. It covers subjects that aren't taught formally but should be. It is definitely not a book intended for people who are sick. If you are showing any of the symptoms listed above on a regular basis, for no apparent reason, then you will certainly find this section useful, but we strongly recommend that you consult your health practitioner.

Don't Panic - There's Good and Bad Anxiety

Anxiety helped our ancestors live in a harsh environment as those who could predict ‚threats' quickly and respond appropriately were more likely to survive. Society has evolved and there is no longer that threat from predators, but the 'threat detection system' is still wired in.

You need anxiety, it's a survival mechanism. Without it, you'd tell your boss exactly how you feel. It triggers your 'fight or flight' response when you do encounter a genuine danger and you need to react quickly to save your life. That's what good anxiety does for you.

However, it can wreak havoc. Modern-day man worries about giving a presentation and his stress response sees it as a threat and activates. He gets this big burst of energy, but experienced as anxiety as opposed to fear. ‚Fear' is when a ‚real' danger is present, anxiety is when you are worried about a ‚threat' that may occur.

Speculation about the future is a complete waste of time. Although our brain is wired to consider the bad things, it can escalate to a point where you simply become afraid of being afraid.

Let's say my partner is half an hour late home from work. I could think, 'there's been an accident' or 'they're having an affair'. I could worry myself sick and get into a frenzy thinking of all the bad things that could have happened. When they eventually walk through the door, I explode. 'Where have you been?' 'What time do you call this?' 'Are you having an affair?' Only to be told that they'd been called into the boss's office to receive a promotion.

How long could such a relationship last? Instead of indulging in speculation, it's better to wait for the facts and just be grateful when your loved one walks through the door.

The Mechanics of Anxiety

Anxiety is an internally generated emotion caused by a perceived or experienced threat or an apprehensive anticipation of future danger.

The best model for understanding how our brain works was developed by Paul MacLean in the 1960s. He identified three different brains that developed during man's evolution.

The reptilian brain controls the body's vital functions - such as the heartbeat and breathing - and it reacts to danger (even when the danger is not real) with an adrenaline response that gives instant energy for the fight or flight response.

The limbic (mammalian) brain records a memory of behaviours that produced agreeable and disagreeable experiences, so it's responsible for emotions. It remembers when you were afraid, so you can respond more quickly next time. Bad experiences are more ingrained as part of the survival mechanism.

The neocortex is responsible for the development of language, imagination, and consciousness. This is the intelligence that makes you human. If you think a lot, plan for the worst case, go over what has occurred in the past or what might occur in the future, you need to look here.

Your 3 Brains in Action

Reptilian   uses adrenaline for a fight or flight response.

Limbic   attaches a feeling and creates a memory.

Neocortex   worries about it happening again so you start to create a learning curve and anticipate anxiety.

For example, say you had a disastrous presentation in front of your boss. Your limbic brain attaches feelings (stress, panic or embarrassment) to that event - both to your boss and to the presentation - and forms deep, emotional memories. Now when you think about your boss or the presentation or tell people about your bad experience, you feel it again. If that occurs again and again, your brain is very quick to learn, and the next time you give a presentation in front of your boss, images and feelings resurface from your emotional memory, and you panic!

If you had immediately forgotten about the presentation, you'd be fine. But that is not a normal response for a conscious brain; your neocortex is intelligent, much more so than your reptilian (which is instinctual), and your mammalian (which stores bad feelings). Your conscious brain searches for meaning; it tries to make sense of what has happened; it fuels your thought processes as you look for answers to 'Was I nervous before I went in?' 'What happened?' It will want you to go over the process again and again in your mind until it has an answer.

Your Brain and Automatic Processes

When you learn something new, your brain creates neural pathways, or connections, to save the memories. Think of those pathways as building blocks. For example, the building blocks that give you the ability to read this page were first laid when you were 4-5 years old. By practising reading you built up and reinforced the building blocks so now you don't analyse each letter to spell a word. you read without thinking about it. The more you practised reading, the stronger the association became, until your practice paid off and reading became automatic. Practice makes perfect! It's the same with anxiety, you create hard-wired neural pathways (building blocks) in your brain. It's not the anxiety that's the problem, but how you habitually think and react that creates problems in your life. How?

Because your thoughts, and the things that you do, affect the wiring structure of your brain.

You Were Not Born Anxious

Things had to be repeated (practised) for you to feel anxiety when there was no real danger. You certainly didn't do this on purpose. You're primed to remember negative experiences rather than positive ones, because this could save you from future harm. It's not the anxiety that is the problem but how you represent it in your mind and how you respond to it. If you feel stressed and anxious when, say, making a presentation, then your brain is alert to this negative situation. The dangers you're responding to are no longer life-threatening situations, but day-to-day experiences: deadlines, money worries, work, relationships, and so on.

All That 'Self-Talk' Going On Inside Your Head

Your anxious brain is always on the lookout for possible 'danger'. When there is no real danger out there, your mind takes over and worries, you expect the worst. Physical symptoms may develop, such as panic attacks. The pathway in your brain for anxiety becomes stronger. It can connect your worries with your body's physical symptoms.

Your brain pays attention when you worry about a meeting or dread going somewhere because you might have an anxiety attack. It creates new pathways relating to anxiety. Now if someone mentions the 'meeting' or the place 'you dread going' your anxiety pathway is activated, and your brain starts your anxiety reflex.

You have your own automatic pilot for worries and the physical symptoms can appear automatically. What your brain pays attention to becomes real to you.

 hotlifestyle.info/ST

Practical Anxiety Management

There's no quick fix. You need to commit to making lifestyle changes that promote a more relaxed way of life. With the right tools you can calm your anxiety so that it no longer affects you as much.

Exercise releases endorphins, hormones that improve how you feel. Taking up jogging will immediately contribute to your physical and mental health. Studies have compared jogging to taking medication without the side effects.

Eating a healthy diet helps keep your brain and gut healthy, both of which can be linked to your mental health.

Cut out stimulants - the obvious ones are caffeine, ginseng, nicotine and alcohol. Chocolate contains theobromine, which is another stimulant.

Drink water as dehydration worsens the symptoms.

Take supplements such as magnesium, kava, ashwaghanda, valerian root, B-complex, St. John's wort, or fish oils.

 hotlifestyle.info/vit/sups

Not everybody will react the same to the above ideas. Try them out to find the one that suits you best.

Anxiety and Sleep

When you're anxious, your heart rate increases, which then causes your brain to 'race'. An alert mind is far too stimulated to sleep. To make matters worse, an active brain triggers other worries, making it even harder to get to sleep.

Once this pattern sets in, bedtime can become an anxious time. So, how can you combat that stress?

You can manage your heart rate by placing your hand on your heart and listening to the beat. Breathe in deeply for four seconds, and then breathe out slowly. Repeat this and relax, you will feel your heart rate slowing.

Eliminate your anxious thoughts by practising the speaking technique. This means voicing the thoughts that would otherwise live in your head. Speaking aloud overrides thinking, which stops your negative thoughts in their tracks. Think through the alphabet in your head, and when you reach 'G', start speaking out loud. What happened to the alphabet? Well, you stopped thinking it in your head, because speaking overrode those thoughts. Use this technique when you start worrying in bed. Instead of thinking 'the monthly sales figures are down', say aloud 'we will find a way to make the sales this month'.

If anxiety is getting in the way of a good night's sleep, then go back to chapter 3 and put those sleep strategies in place.

Desensitization

Anxiety can be linked to an obvious trigger. In the real world anxiety is the reason you don't talk to that person you fancy, or make that big telephone call, or get on stage to give a presentation. The fear of rejection and failure stop us doing many of those things that would be game changers.

Desensitization is a procedure developed by Joseph Wolpe to reduce the exaggerated responses (triggers) that cause anxiety. Follow a three-step plan to get your mind and body used to the triggers so that they no longer create that involuntary anxiety reaction. You can do it in the comfort of your home. First, you need to make sure you're ready to commit to it. You must not cheat and only move on when you're ready.

Step 1 Anxiety Hierarchy - First, construct an anxiety hierarchy, which is a list of those situations that lead up to your target situation. Then rank them in order, from the least disturbing to the most disturbing.

Step 2 Relaxation Training - Learn deep muscle relaxation.

Step 3 Desensitization Sessions - You then go through a series of desensitization sessions.

You can read more about this desensitization procedure on:

 hotlifestyle.info/des

Breathing for Relaxation

We will talk a lot about breathing techniques stemming from yoga. Research has shown that how you breathe is intricately connected to your emotional state. You can control your state by changing your breathing pattern. If you breathe in a calm, controlled manner, surrounded by an aroma (real or imagined), savouring each deep slow breath, it has a profound calming effect. Calming natural essential oil fragrances are lavender, camomile, ylang ylang, lemon, yuzu, clary sage, or jasmine.

Deep Breathing

Sit down with your back straight, place one hand on your stomach. Breathe in slowly from the abdomen and through your nose for a count of 7, fill your lungs with as much air as possible. Breathe so that you feel your lower abdomen rise and fall. Then hold it for a few seconds and breathe out slowly through your mouth, for a count of 11 (breathe out like you're whistling). Repeat 10 times.

CO_2 Rebreathing

Erratic breathing, often the result of an anxiety attack can cause hyperventilation, which causes too much oxygen to enter your blood, giving you symptoms like dizziness and a rapid heartbeat. Hold a paper bag over your nose and mouth while you breathe, keep breathing normally to regain your carbon dioxide levels.

Setting Goals

The above are all proven ways to deal with anxiety, but don't expect a change just from reading this book, or by doing any of the exercises in isolation. Simply understanding the problem won't free you of it. Stop focusing on the problem, and start to focus on the solution.

Begin with short-term, self-help solutions, such as regular exercise, quality sleep, and managing your diet - does this sound familiar?

Long-term self-help solutions, such as breathing training, relaxation techniques, and desensitization will help you further. If these measures don't give you the result you're looking for then seek advice from a health practitioner. Be aware though, taking medication to fight anxiety simply masks the symptoms without dealing with the cause.

Talking about your anxiety with a practitioner may be helpful. Find someone who uses techniques such as NLP or CBT for quicker positive results.

It's never a bad idea to do an inventory of your typical worries, to get a sense of where you are on the spectrum, or what particular situations make you anxious. It can be helpful to be familiar with your internal states and become mindful of what they might be trying to tell you.

Let's Sum Up

Anxiety is a response to perceived danger or fear.

The symptoms of anxiety that manifest become the issue.

The symptoms can cause a downward spiral of more fear.

Understand how your 3 brains work to create worry.

Fear of fear inhibits you from attempting bigger goals.

Begin with step one of practical anxiety management.

Desensitization - anxiety cannot exist when you're relaxed.

Breathing techniques can help alleviate symptoms.

Talking about your worries can put them in perspective.

Certain aromas and music can have a calming effect.

What You Can Achieve

Make bolder decisions in your life with confidence.

Pursue game-changing strategies.

Make the first move and ask someone out for a date.

Do nothing, then nothing will change

~ Paul McQueen

CHAPTER FIVE

Wellbeing

Water Water Everywhere

The main reason that most of us don't drink enough fluid is surprisingly simple, we don't monitor how much we drink in a day. Carrying a litre bottle around with us seems to make drinking a daunting task, and who can remember how many of the eight required glasses they've drunk?

A minimum of 1.5 litres of water is required daily just to carry out basic functions like body temperature regulation, transport of nutrients, and removal of waste (detox). We recommend drinking at least 2 litres per day for the average adult living in a temperate climate. This amount ensures your kidneys have enough fluid to flush out harmful toxins.

So, the best detox is a large glass (1 pint /0.5 litre) of lukewarm water first thing in the morning the minute you get up. Then wait 30 minutes before you have breakfast.

Be aware of diuretics. Drinks containing alcohol or hot drinks such as tea or coffee increase the need to urinate, making you lose fluids. Plain tap water is always the best option.

Use a filter for tap water. The chemicals used to purify water and kill the bacteria also affect the good bacteria in your gut.

**If you take nothing else away with you
from this book, then it should be this:**

Drink, Drink, Drink

Detoxification

The idea that you can flush your alcohol-drenched liver of impurities and leave your kidneys squeaky clean with a few cups of herbal tea or pills is utter nonsense. There are some unscrupulous marketeers who use the word 'detox' as a pseudo-medical concept to sell something for which there is no evidence that it works. Don't waste your money on so-called 'detox regimes'. You already have a fantastic 'detox' system, if you didn't, you'd be in hospital. Drinking plenty of water, eating healthy and limiting alcohol to a minimum is all the detox you need.

Inflammation and the Right Foods

The word inflammation has been used a few times and I thought I should expand on this important subject. There are two types of inflammation, 'clinical' and 'sub-clinical'. We will be discussing the latter in some detail.

Clinical Inflammation

You hit your knee and your immune system springs into action, it becomes inflamed, painful, and swells up. This is a normal and effective response that facilitates healing.

Sub-Clinical (Chronic) Inflammation

Sub-clinical, or chronic, inflammation is less obvious since it has no visible signs or symptoms. It is something we ALL have in varying degrees and it can last for months or years if we fail to address the cause. Think of it as an internal irritant that turns on the disease process, causing chronic health issues associated with ageing. It is systemic and affects your organs and internal structures. Chronic inflammation increases the risk of arthritis, heart disease, cancer, diabetes, hypothyroidism, and weight gain.

Despite the proven connection between diet and sub-clinical inflammation, doctors don't always consider diet in response to these ailments.

What Causes Sub-Clinical Inflammation?

Dietary and environmental toxins build up in the body, turning the immune system on and keeping it highly reactive. A poor diet, stress, a sedentary (couch potato) lifestyle all contribute to chronic inflammation.

Researchers believe it is due to an overactive immune system flooding the body with defence cells and hormones that damage tissues. The Western-type diet - high in sugar, fried foods, refined grains (GPS), and high-fat dairy products - promotes high levels of inflammation. Many people still choose convenience over health. Fast foods and convenience foods make up a significant and unhealthy proportion of our diet.

You might compare it to feeding the cat with lettuce. It's the wrong food for the animal. We humans are eating foods containing well known allergens that cause our levels of inflammation to increase.

On the other hand, the Mediterranean diet, green leafy vegetables, and fish, and low in red meat and butter, with moderate alcohol and moderate to high olive oil intake, shows lower levels of inflammation.

Everything in Moderation

Foods that promote inflammation are robbing you of your vitality and making you ill. Be aware of them and try to eat less of them. Keep reading, for some fantastic alternatives.

Inflammation-Causing Foods

Grains
Avoid milled refined grains (a process that removes the bran and germ to give it a finer texture), such as white flour, white bread, white rice, corn flakes, or spaghetti. Whole grains can be eaten in moderation, such as wholewheat bread, buckwheat, oats, millet, brown or wild rice, spelt, amaranth.

Potatoes
Potatoes have a high GI rating, so overeating them stimulates a big insulin response that, over time, leads to inflammation. In small amounts, served in their skins, and as part of a healthy diet, they aren't a problem.

Sugar and Refined Starch
Consuming soda, snack bars, candy, baked sweets, sucrose, and lactose leads to a rapid increase in blood sugar; which, in turn, causes insulin levels to rise and triggers an immune response. The result is a pro-inflammatory response leading to chronic inflammation. Avoid anything with added or artificial sweeteners.

One thing most people don't realize is how damaging fructose (fruit sugars) can be, so they should be eaten in moderation. Here is a list of foods containing high levels of fructose:

 hotlifestyle.info/FR

Vegetable Oil

Found in mayonnaise, salad dressings, barbecue sauce, and potato chips, vegetable oil has high concentrations of the inflammatory fat omega-6. The healthy alternative is olive oil.

Dairy Products

While moderate amounts of yogurt with gut-healing probiotics help decrease inflammation, full-fat dairy products, soft cheeses, yogurt, butter, ice cream - is a source of inflammation-inducing saturated fats and decreases the levels of our good gut bacteria, which are key players in reducing inflammation.

Red Meat

Eating red meat produces a chemical called 'Neu5gc', to which the body produces an inflammatory immune response.

Processed or Fast Foods? Avoid at all cost!

Don't despair! Everything in moderation.

I can hear you now. 'So, what can I eat? No chips, no milk, yet another group of foods on the watch list.' There are several lifestyle factors contributing to inflammation that are under your control. Get plenty of sleep, learn to relax more, if you smoke then quit, and engage in regular exercise. Diet is only part of the mix. By all means eat your favourite foods just in moderation. Use the Hotlifestyle Healthy Shopping List to guide you. See the link to download a print friendly version of it on the next page.

Time for a Healthy Anti-Inflammatory Diet

Green Leafy Vegetables
Spinach, kale, romaine lettuce, and Swiss chard are full of natural anti-inflammatory agents and rich in antioxidants.

Cruciferous Veggies
Cauliflower, cabbage, garden cress, bok choy, broccoli, Brussels sprouts, celery are high in antioxidants, and all have a natural detoxifying effect.

Fish
Fatty fish, such as wild salmon, mackerel, tuna and sardines, are high in omega-3s.

Nuts
Focus particularly on walnuts (be careful if watching your weight is an issue and have no more than seven a day), also good are almonds, Brazil nuts, cashews.

Superfoods
All fruits and vegetables should be considered superfoods. Get away from processed foods and replace them with fruit and veggies from your local supermarket.

Download or print the Hotlifestyle Healthy Shopping List:

 hotlifestyle.info/HD

Proteolytic Enzymes

If you're like me, you'll have read this title and switched off. The first study that I read was from 1989 (Oxford University), meaning we have known about them for a long time and they are very important. Proteolytic enzymes are produced naturally in the body and, among other things, they help break down protein in the digestive system. They are found in certain foods, and are available as supplements (some contain a single type, others contain a combination).

Many studies show that taking them helps to reduce chronic inflammation and the symptoms related to inflammatory conditions. These include IBS, muscle soreness, indigestion, and gas. Depending on your goals, it could be really beneficial to include them in your diet.

Excellent natural sources are: papaya, pineapple, kiwi, and fermented foods. Other sources include: bromelain, turmeric, devil's claw, boswellia extract, ginger extract, and rutin.

 hotlifestyle.info/vit/PE

Consult your doctor before taking proteolytic enzyme supplements, as they can have side effects and may not be compatible with certain prescribed medications.

Let's Sum Up

Drink at least 2 litres of fluid each day.

Your liver is an excellent detox tool, support it by drinking.

Sub-clinical inflammation could be causing your problems.

Eat fewer foods that contribute to sub-clinical inflammation.

Eat more foods that are anti-inflammatory.

Proteolytic enzymes help reduce sub-clinical inflammation.

Learn which enzymes are used for each particular case.

Go shopping with the Hotlifestyle Healthy Shopping List.

Try the 30-day vitality challenge on the next page.

What You Can Achieve

Making small changes in diet can have a big impact.

Preventative measures help slow degenerative illnesses.

Share the Healthy Shopping List with your friends.

Download it here:

 hotlifestyle.info/HD

Final Thoughts On Vitality

Vitality should be top of your list as part of achieving a Hotlifestyle. If you don't maintain long-term good health, nothing else will be achievable. You should have learned a lot about yourself and be experimenting to find out what works best for you. We've put some of the concepts into easy to follow lists for you to act on. Print them out and use them.

We are all different, what works for one may not necessarily work for another. With regard to diet we recommend that you make a slow transition by including the types of foods listed on the 'Hotlifestyle Healthy Shopping List' into your daily routine. At least dip your toe in the water and try a few each week.

Start to eat less of those foods that are not recommended, those with a high GI rating or GPS foods.

It shouldn't require a book like this to tell you that you need regular exercise. I know time is always an issue, but it is about building habits that benefit you. The pointers here should inspire you to at least walk the stairs more often instead of taking the lift, for example.

Simply reading this book is not enough, you must act. We have put together a challenge to get you started on your journey to embracing healthy habits.

The 30-Day Vitality Challenge

Water

Start each day with a pint/0.5 litre of lukewarm water.

Monitor your drinking to ensure that you drink a minimum of 2 litres/day; consider carrying a 1 litre bottle around with you. Use a filter for drinking tap water.

Refined Sugars

Reduce your intake of refined sugar by half.

One spoon instead of two in tea or coffee for example. I find that lactose-free milk is sweeter and use less sugar because of it, besides it being healthier.

Exercise

Go the extra mile and walk short distances instead of driving. Use the stairs more and take the lift less.

Stimulants

Cut down stimulants by 20% each on alcohol, tobacco, and coffee/tea.

Sleep

Go to bed at the same time each night; wake up at the same time too - this includes weekends.

BOOK TWO

LIFESKILLS

Competence Builds Confidence

INTRODUCTION

Look at us, the result of two million years of evolution and some of us can't even boil an egg!

Any skill set that helps improve your quality of life is a lifeskill. It helps you deal better with others and propels you to your full potential. Different skills are more relevant at different stages of your life. Perhaps the most important lifeskill is the ability and willingness to leave your comfort zone and embrace change. You already possess a multitude of skills, such as organizational skills, time management, study skills, leadership skills... and there are many others to be learned. Lifeskills are not formally taught in school, but we think that they should be.

Things that are not considered lifeskills but everyone would benefit from learning them include:

➢ 10-fingered touch typing on a full size keyboard
➢ Typing numbers on a keypad, blindfold
➢ The phonetic alphabet: A for alfa, B for bravo, etc.
➢ The basics of Microsoft Office® and cyber security
➢ Five knots: tie, bow tie, figure-eight, reef knot, bowline
➢ Special licences in advanced driving, sailing, flying ...

We discuss many important lifeskills in this book to help you become the best version of yourself.

*Because your personality
isn't the first thing people see*

~ Paul McQueen

———————————

CHAPTER SIX

Appearance

Yes, It Matters

Deep down, we would all like to think that appearance doesn't matter and as youngsters we're told things like not to judge a book by its cover. The sad fact is, people are judging you all the time, whether it's at work, flirting across a crowded room, or going to the bank for a loan, they just can't help it. People make assumptions about you in a split second based upon your appearance. If you look the part and behave appropriately for the occasion, you're far more likely to receive better service, command more respect, and get what you want. The impression you make on your first encounter depends on your appearance.

The Mechanics of First Encounters

The thing about first impressions, is that there is absolutely no second chance. They can make or break meetings, potential friendships, or even a date. To help us deal with first encounters we have evolved an instinct to make a snap judgement as our survival might just depend on it. We all need to answer two questions regarding the characteristics of the person standing in front of us:

Intention   What are this person's intentions toward me? How lovable (warm, trustworthy) are they?

Capability   Are they capable of acting on those intentions? How fearsome (strong, competent) are they?

These two assessments decide our emotional and behavioural reactions toward other people, groups, and even companies. These opinions form in a split second. Our neocortex (our conscious brain) can't weigh up someone's true merits so it relies on the limbic (mammalian) brain, which uses experience and stereotypes (based on race, gender, bias, etc.) to 'rate' the person ‚high' or ‚low' on imaginary scales of ‚intention' and ‚capability'. Global research has shown that this is a very common way of thinking.

The decision reached, albeit based mainly on appearance (the meeting's location may also play a role), determines whether, and how, another person will interact with you. Studies have shown that our snap judgements of other people's characteristics are more often than not incredibly accurate. Once this newly formed opinion is embedded, it's hard to change someone's mind. This is why first impressions are so important because they stick.

There is a willingness to help people who are considered as ‚warm' and shut out those who are ‚cold'. We want to associate with people perceived as ‚competent' and ignore those considered ‚incompetent'. This is obviously irrational and is based on perceived ideas, which include all our prejudices. Inaccurate warmth/competence judgements can lead to you trusting untrustworthy people or undervaluing potentially important connections. Remember the sales girl in Zurich who refused to serve Oprah Winfrey?

Research has brought to light a profound anomaly. People view warmth and competence as inversely related. Which means, if you are seen as having a surplus of one trait then you must have a deficit of the other. If you are too nice in the workplace, then you're unlikely to be perceived as competent. The nicer you are the worse it gets. It's obvious from this that you must strike a balance.

So, what is the first thing people notice on a first encounter?

Cleanliness is Next To ...

... hopefully, the person sitting next to you on the plane. I always end up sitting next to the smelly person. It's not that they don't shower regularly, either they smell overwhelmingly of cigarette smoke or their jacket/trousers haven't been cleaned recently. Funny thing is, they don't seem to notice it themselves. Sweat that has collected over a long period can smell like a corpse. Make sure that YOU don't become that smelly person on the plane and take your coats and trousers to the cleaners regularly.

Be critical of how you smell because, no one is going to tell you, they will just avoid you. If you are overweight and unfit, then you will sweat more during the hot summer months. Do your colleagues - and any potential lover - a favour and shower a little more often.

Studies show that women rate a male's scent as the #1 factor when searching for a potential partner, men on the other hand are more visual. There are a thousand different fragrances available. Find one that suits your personality - or ask the sales person for advice, that's what they're there for.

Keeping your hands clean and presentable is extremely important when meeting others. Shaking hands with someone who has 'nail fungus' is really gross.

Are you a nail biter? It is a habit that disgusts many people. Try to identify at which times you bite your nails then create another response, like squeezing a pen or sucking a mint. Or invest in a bitter-tasting, clear nail polish. Unkempt hands and nails can make you look uneducated (less competent). Invest in a hand cream as dry cracked skin will really let you down.

Dare we mention feet? Should we really have to mention them? Being cooped up for hours on end, encased in leather, it's no wonder that some of us suffer with foot odour. The obvious cure is washing regularly but there are also foot odour insoles and sprays available to combat excessive perspiration which is the main cause of smelly feet. There, I said it!

Hair. Do you wear it as your crowning glory, with confidence, or is every day a bad hair day and you look like a lazy bum with low self-esteem? Studies show that your hairstyle is an accurate reflection of your personality. Reason enough to invest some time and money in it. Healthy, shiny, well-groomed hair can take months to achieve and depends on many of the factors discussed in the vitality section. Eating healthily, especially getting enough omega 3, and drinking enough fluids will affect hair quality. Consider only washing it twice a week and using a deep conditioner (apply castor oil an hour before washing) once a week will help with frizz, as will letting your hair dry naturally using the hairdryer as sparingly as possible.

Choosing the right hair cut for your face requires time and thought. A good stylist can advise on how to enhance your facial features. Don't be afraid to experiment. Try something bold but remain authentic as a wild hairstyle with conservative cloths sends a confusing message and won't necessarily make you more attractive.

Clothes Make the Man (and the Woman)

There are times in your life when you will have to conform and perform. So, when you have got to get it right first time, then get it right with the correct attire.

➢ The right clothing gets you noticed and boosts confidence

➢ You will be judged on your dress sense

➢ Formal attire increases status and attractiveness

➢ Clothes are a statement of your position and who you are

➢ Well-dressed people are perceived as more competent

Dress to Impress

One study (Townsend and Levy) found that men who dressed to indicate high socioeconomic status (suit or other formal dress) were rated as significantly more attractive by females and more appealing as potential relationship partners. Similar effects did not occur with male ratings of women.

The University of Sunderland in England studied 'The White-Coat Effect' to see if patients in front of a formally dressed doctor were less likely to be open and honest about their symptoms than with a doctor in casual attire.

Participants were shown photos of doctors in three different outfits:

➢ standard doctor's attire with a white coat

➢ suit with white shirt and tie, or a blouse in the case of female doctors

➢ blue jeans, plain white T-shirt, and trainers

The participants were asked to say whether they felt the doctor looked like an authority, seemed friendly, was attractive. They found that casually dressed doctors did not get disclosure from patients. Casual dress decreased perceptions of authority, friendliness, attractiveness, and trust. A willingness to disclose symptoms went in favour of those dressed authoritatively. The study also concluded that status and authority were positively related to friendliness and trustworthiness.

To take this a step further, in any situation where authority, status, and trustworthiness are important - for example in business, law, and other professions - wearing formal attire portrays all these attributes.

You need to take on board all those points while remaining 100% authentic to who YOU are and not feeling like a fraud wearing a costume.

Choosing a Man's Wardrobe

Let's face it, when it comes to creating a wardrobe, men have it easy. A suit, a decent jacket, a good pair of jeans, some tasteful underwear and socks, and one pair of formal shoes. The 'professional' look is easily established with the suit and tie.

But is it always wise to be dressed up to the nines? Being too formal on the wrong occasion can work against you, especially if the other party feels intimidated by you. Your wardrobe should be influenced by your environment. I believe you should always dress one notch above the standard dress code for that environment. Adding small details to your outfit shows a level of class. It can be as simple as tucking your shirt in your trousers if you work on the factory floor. Wearing a tie-pin or cufflinks shows that you're taking care of your appearance.

What colour suit should you buy? Black suits are the most formal and should not be worn as daily office wear. Want to make a big impression? Then a black suit, white shirt, and tie will achieve this. A classic alternative for formal events is the dark blue suit with cognac brown shoes, which you'll find fits most occasions.

If you only have one suit, then it should be single-breasted and charcoal grey. It is the perfect attire for every occasion, it is smart but combines well with casual shoes or jeans for dress-down Fridays. If you can, you should also buy the waistcoat for those occasions when you really want to up your game. A charcoal grey suit combined with burgundy or black shoes and a matching tie shows you have arrived. It should certainly be your first choice for job interviews. If you're office based it is worth buying one jacket with two pairs of trousers (remember what was said about cleaning?).

The classic, single-breasted, navy-blue blazer is so versatile that you can build an entire wardrobe around it. Given its iconic status, it can be worn at any age, to both casual and many formal events. The key is to combine it with colours that contrast with the navy-blue, you don't want to give the impression that you are making it into a suit. Experiment with combinations, light-coloured shirts, light-blue or white looks great, and light- or dark-grey trousers or light-blue jeans. Shoes can be either black with the grey trousers or burgundy with jeans to add a personal touch. On cooler days try a long-sleeve sweater with a round neck. A popular combination is a plain white crew-cut T-shirt with the blazer for a relaxed feel. A good quality blazer is great value and will last for years.

 hotlifestyle.info/life/BZ

Many men find it hard to create the right look themselves. It can also be very time consuming. You might consider a consultation with a stylist to point you in the right direction.

Choose the right fabrics. Opting for 100% worsted wool may cost a little more, but it will hang better and hold its shape longer, it also lets your skin breathe in summer. Using polyester and synthetic fabrics are a bad idea.

What will let you down the most when trying to dress up is the fit. If the jacket is too short or the sleeves are too long or it is too tight around the middle then, regardless of how much you paid, it will make a bad impression. If your clothes don't fit, then get them adjusted. Jackets and trousers can be let out as well as taken in. With off the rack suits it is unlikely that you will find a perfect fit so allow some money in the budget for alterations. Most shops offer this service for a small fee.
Further reading on the right fit can be found on:

 hotlifestyle.info/fit

Often, your first encounter with someone is not planned. You simply never know when you might meet your future boss or business partner or that special person who will sweep you off your feet. Looking good is not just for planned occasions, you should make an effort to look good every day. Just a little extra effort when you dress, especially with accessories, will boost your confidence and certainly get you noticed.

Must-Have Accessories for Men

Here's your chance to add a unique personal touch to highlight your look. Being well accessorized is just one of those aspects of being a well-groomed adult that will make you stand out from the crowd. Purchase each item carefully, pay as much as your budget allows, as quality will be noticed. Include a splash of red. Even the smallest amount of red makes you look more confident.

Elegant classic belts made of real leather matched to your shoes will last for years. A simple belt buckle with a single square frame and prong will fit every occasion.

Own a serious dress watch. Thin with a simple clear dial, and a leather strap, which could also match those burgundy shoes. Worn to impress, you will need it at some point.

Elegant leather gloves demonstrates class in a subtle way. They keep your hands warm and skin healthy in winter.

A cashmere or wool scarf to complement your jacket.

Sunglasses that are well made and stylish are absolutely essential for an air of sophistication.

The type of wallet a man carries says a lot about him. A simple leather wallet (brown or black) with space for cards.

Wearing a signature scent makes you memorable. Take time to find the right one for you.

Socks can help draw attention to your shoes and often make or break an outfit. The safe option is dark, single tone.

Boxer briefs, especially in darker colours can be simply irresistible. Briefs and not boxer shorts!

Choosing a Woman's Wardrobe

In today's workplace, it can be tricky choosing the right outfit, because many companies follow the trend of casual wear and, whether you like it or not, your appearance plays a decisive role in your success. Getting it wrong can hurt your chances of promotion. If the office dress is conservative you may need to adapt your look to fit the corporate environment, regardless of your personal sense of style. You should always dress to impress, make sure that your 'professional appearance' supports your 'professional accomplishments' and doesn't emphasize the 'wrong assets'. Know your employer's dress code and dress one notch above, especially for interviews.

Whenever you start a new job, observe the dress code of your immediate superiors. This will tell you the appropriate level of formality you should follow. Invest in a standard women's suit, tailored dresses, skirts with a blouse and jacket. Standard business attire is more polished and professional-looking than casual dress. When in doubt, stick with standard professional business attire.

Dress shabbily and they remember the dress.
Dress impeccably and they remember
the woman

~ Coco Chanel

Professional Business Attire

Be classic and understated, choose plain, muted colours over bright patterns, keep make-up and accessories to a minimum. You should aim for a professional and sophisticated look. Do make sure your clothes fit properly.

The Business Suit

A well-tailored blazer with matching skirt or trousers in either black, navy, or dark grey, made of wool, are a solid base for the well-dressed woman. Make sure that the blazer fits snugly to your shoulders without overhanging. You should be able to comfortably fasten any front button, and the sleeves should end at your wrist, not covering your hands. It's important to alter trousers to fit your height and the height of the shoes you will be wearing. Skirts shouldn't be more than two finger-widths above the knee and they should be worn with dark or nude-coloured, plain hosiery.

Formal Business Tops

A buttoned-up shirt or blouse made from a cotton blend, rayon, or silk complements a business suit perfectly. Coordinate the colour or pattern so it does not clash with your suit. Solid colours of white, light blue or light pink are always a safe bet. There's no hard and fast rule about which neckline to choose, just avoid revealing too much cleavage.

Shoes

Dark-coloured leather pumps are an essential basic of every professional woman's wardrobe. They should match your outfit and, preferably, be close-toe style. Shoes with two to four inch heels are acceptable, but it does depend on your height, and flats may be the most appropriate.

Professional Casual Attire

Separates

There are a multitude of possibilities here, two contrasting items of clothing, such as a skirt with a cardigan or a trendy pair of trousers combined with a long-sleeved blouse. Nice dresses can make a refreshing change in the office but should not be sleeveless, and the rules for length and cleavage still apply. Subtle prints, patterns with stripes or checks, and solid colours are all fine on condition there is a certain harmony. Basically, anything goes, except for denim, neon colours, loud prints, see-through, off-shoulder and tummy-baring tops.

Shoes

Make them an expression of your personality while keeping them simple. Comfortable flats, loafers, or pumps of any colour that matches your outfit, with closed toes.

Accessories

Accessories are meant to complement your outfit, not overpower it. Keep earrings small, subtle, and above the earlobe. As a successful woman, you should definitely own an elegant, conservative watch. It is better to wear no jewellery than wear too much.

Handbags

Should be large enough to fit A4-sized documents without folding. Preferably made of quality leather in a neutral colour, like black or brown. It should have a clasp or zip so that others can't easily see the contents. A man's briefcase can be too masculine, there are many beautifully made briefcases for women on the market. Don't dress like a man!

Hair and Nails

When dressing for the office, your hairstyle should be neat and conservative, preferably off the face. Hair sprays with an overpowering scent send the wrong message. Never leave the house with wet hair, besides being unhealthy, it gives the impression that you don't have your life together. If you have to wear hair accessories, choose sleek metal headbands and basic black ponytail ties, avoid the glittery stuff. Nails should be well-groomed and if you use nail polish choose a beige tone or a clear coat. Super long nails are simply a no go.

Posture and Body Language

A poor self-image can be reflected in our posture. The way you carry yourself leaves an impression on everyone you meet. We'll discuss this important subject in more depth later.

How you view yourself is important to your success and happiness. If every time you look in a mirror you are pleased with what you see it will have a huge effect on your psyche. This goes as much for posture and body language as it does for your clothes. If you feel good about yourself when meeting others for the first time they will pick up on this. It will also build up your confidence, which breeds confidence. Sit up straight, don't slouch, and remember to smile to make a positive first impression that should make you memorable in the mind of anyone you meet.

THE BOTTOM LINE

You still haven't opened your mouth and your non-verbal cues are screaming out across the room.

Ask yourself this, are they communicating the message you want to convey?

Let's Sum Up

Be critical of your appearance, as first impressions count.

Check your body odour and grooming.

Clothes are one criterion that you will be judged upon.

Choose high-quality fabrics, such as wool, cotton, or silk.

The fit of your clothes is of paramount importance.

Choose versatile styles that allow you to dress up and down.

The navy-blue blazer is versatile and makes a statement.

The few accessories you do buy should be of a good quality.

Perfume, cologne, and jewellery should be discreet.

Own an elegant, conservative watch.

Choose the right attire for the occasion.

Don't wear the same outfit two days running, people notice.

Be aware of your body language during first encounters.

Remain 100% authentic to who YOU are.

What You Can Achieve

Make a lasting impression on everyone you meet.

Gain more respect and success by dressing appropriately.

It's not stress that kills us,
it's our reaction to it

~ Hans Selye

CHAPTER SEVEN

Stress & Emotions

When the Pressure's On

Doctor Hans Selye, from Vienna, Austria, was the first to associate a biological response with stressors and believed that stress could be either good or bad. He came up with the term ,stress' in the 1930s. He determined that stress can be positive, for example by pushing you to perform better. Healthy stress doesn't overwhelm your life and some people need the pressure of stress for motivation. Think of deadlines when you have to get something done, or targets you have to achieve. They are designed to create pressure that makes you perform better.

The Mechanics of Stress

Stress is defined as a specific response to an external stimulus. It manifests as a physical response when you think you're being attacked.

The line between stressful and anxious emotions is often blurred because they cause similar symptoms, such as rapid breathing and increased heart rate. The cause of acute stress is plainly different from the cause of anxiety. Stress is the result of how we deal with pressure in our day-to-day lives and you can identify and deal with what is causing it, ,the trigger'. Anxiety comes from feelings of helplessness and worry that continue after the stressor is gone. The two emotions come from two different places and, despite the differences, many people mistakenly use the terms interchangeably.

Life-threatening situations can cause stress and trigger the ,fight or flight' instinct in us by releasing adrenalin and cortisol, which give us a burst of energy to help us survive.

Responses to Inappropriate Levels of Pressure

We will all experience pressure in our lives to varying degrees. More pressure means more stress, but what is stressful to one person may not be perceived as stressful to another. What causes you stress depends, in part, on your perceptions and how you cope with the stressors that do affect you. There's a whole list of things that are particularly stressful, like losing your job, getting a divorce, or money problems. The most stressful encounters in life are generally due to unplanned changes in your personal circumstances. Stress is accumulative and often emotionally charged but nowadays not a question of survival.

 hotlifestyle.info/stress

There can come a point, when stress stops being helpful and starts causing problems, affecting your health and quality of life. The point when you 'stress out' differs from person to person. Some people have high tolerance levels and can roll with life's punches, while others struggle to cope with minor obstacles. There are even those who deliberately pursue a high-stress lifestyle for the sheer thrill of it.

Long-term stress creates elevated levels of adrenalin and cortisol (known as the stress hormone), which can lead to serious health issues. Many people are unaware that they're suffering from the results of stress and go to the doctor with symptoms of indigestion, back pain, headaches, and so on. The symptoms of stress are broad and not always obvious.

It's important that you become aware of the early warning signs of stress overload, because they can sneak up on you. Very often symptoms become a normal part of your everyday life and are not taken seriously enough.

The many common symptoms of stress can include:

Emotional Symptoms

Depression, general unhappiness, or frequent crying spells
Overreaction to petty annoyances or wild mood swings
Excessive gambling or impulse buying
Feelings of loneliness, worthlessness, or defensiveness

Physical Symptoms

Neckache, back pain, muscle spasms, chest pain
Light headedness, faintness, dizziness
Difficulty breathing, frequent sighing, rapid heart rate
Frequent colds, infections, herpes sores
Constant tiredness, weakness, fatigue

Behavioural Symptoms

Obsessive or compulsive behaviour, gritting/grinding teeth
Insomnia, nightmares, disturbing dreams
Increased smoking, alcohol, or drug use
Nervous habits, fidgeting, feet tapping
Social withdrawal and isolation

Cognitive Symptoms

Forgetfulness, disorganization, confusion
Difficulty concentrating or making decisions
Trouble learning new information
Feeling overloaded, overwhelmed, or pessimistic
Excess anxiety, worry, guilt, nervousness

Four Different Measures of Stress

Acute Stress

In small doses, this can be thrilling. Bungee jumping or roller coaster rides create this kind of stress. It is also generated by the demands of a looming deadline or a pending speech, or after a car crash. It is short-lived and generally doesn't leave long-lasting scars. Symptoms are mild, such as stomach aches, gut and bowel problems, headaches, sweaty palms, palpitations.

Episodic Acute Stress

Do you suffer acute stress on a regular basis, maybe because you have bitten off more than you can chew and never seem to get on top of your workload? Are you a ‚Type A' personality (Friedman and Rosenman), always on the go, competitive to an extreme, aggressive, and impatient? For people with Type A behaviour patterns, episodic acute stress is the natural state: overexcited, short-tempered, and irritable; with frequent headaches, hypertension, and chest pain. It is very difficult for a Type A personality to change, as they identify with their condition completely, believing it is simply the way they are. They are generally very successful in the workplace but less so when it comes to personal relationships.

 hotlifestyle.info/life/WS

Chronic Stress

Have you spent years in a job you despise or a loveless marriage? Chronic stress is associated with never-ending problems, when you can't see a light at the end of the tunnel, and all hope is gone. It can wear you down to the point of suicide. You can live in such conditions for years, getting used to the drudgery of your life, but this kind of stress is slowly killing you; you can suffer a heart attack, a stroke, or become prone to outbursts of violence. The symptoms of chronic stress are difficult to treat and may require extended medical, as well as behavioural, treatment and need stress management help from a professional.

Burnout

When you have reached this stage, then your complaints have been present for a long time and have become chronic. Past warnings have been ignored and you're completely exhausted. You are living in a daze, you don't know what day it is half the time, and your ability to plan the future, organize yourself, or set goals has been affected. You probably haven't had a good night's sleep in ages and your job has become intolerable.

This stage should be the ultimate warning signal to make you stop and think about who you are versus who you want to be, before you suffer a complete psychological breakdown. Take stock of your life and seek professional help immediately.

Practical Stress Management

Beef Up Your Stress Tolerance Levels

Take responsibility for your life. If you feel that your circumstances are controlling you, and not the other way around then you are more likely to feel overwhelmed. Taking responsibility and controlling your destiny will boost your confidence and alleviate stress.

Take on the challenge and embrace change. Having a positive outlook on life, looking for solutions and not problems is key to reducing stress. Life will throw things your way no matter who you are, it's the way you deal with them that makes the difference. Stop saying, why me?

Create a support network of friends and family. Having reliable people around you to talk with can help with life's pressures. Often, just venting your frustrations can lower stress levels.

Manage your expectations. Having a clear understanding of the mechanics of your stress and how long you can expect it to last, makes it easier to deal with.

Deal with your emotions. If you react emotionally to everything people say to you, learn how to become emotionally intelligent.

 hotlifestyle.info/life/EQ

If you're suffering from stress, then read the advice given for anxiety - take enough exercise, eat a healthy diet, cut out stimulants, drink at least two litres of water a day, and take supplements.

What Kind of Stress Do You Experience?

In other words, how do you react under pressure? People have different responses to different pressures. Understanding your response is key to deciding how you should deal with it. It is important you learn to relax. I hear you now, 'but I relax every night in front of the telly'. That's good, but it's not going to give you the psychological benefits of deep relaxation. Once you master one of the relaxation techniques, then you will have an 'aha!' moment and understand the difference.

We have already mentioned the fight or flight response, when your brain weighs up the best course of action in a split second, and then you react. What strategy do you tend to choose?

Fight

Do you get angry, aggressive, impatient, shout a lot, or throw things around when you're under pressure? This is typical behaviour from a ,Type A' personality. You need to quiet down. Deep breathing, progressive muscle relaxation, or meditation would be useful.

Flight

Does pressure make you feel sad or withdrawn, or even give you feelings of being completely spaced out? Which makes you a 'Type B' personality. Try rhythmic exercise (like aerobic training or jogging), power yoga, a massage, or mindfulness. You will probably respond better to activities that stimulate your nervous system as opposed to too much relaxation.

Which Relaxation Technique Suits You Best?

If your stress response is being activated every day, then over time it will take its toll on your emotional health. After all, stress is a natural part of our lives, it's unavoidable. Just as your body has a stress response you also have a natural relaxation response. You've already had your first encounter with a relaxation response when you used the 7/11 deep breathing technique.

When you are in a state of deep relaxation, stress cannot exist. You can balance your body and mind by practising these techniques. When you activate a relaxation response your heart rate will slow, breathing is easier and slower, you become completely relaxed, and your blood pressure normalizes.

Progressive Muscle Relaxation

This is a technique that creates a relaxation response by tightening and relaxing muscle groups, starting with your feet and working up your body. Tense muscles are one of the side effects of stress and using progressive muscle relaxation allows you to get a feel for the difference between being tense and being relaxed. You need about 15 minutes to complete the exercise.

➢ Remove your shoes and loosen your clothing

➢ Lie down on a mat on the floor or on your bed

➢ Put your hand on your stomach and breathe deeply for 2 minutes from your abdomen so your hand rises and falls

➢ Start by tightly clenching the muscles in your right foot

➢ Focus on the tension built up and hold for 5 seconds

➢ Release the tension and really relax your right foot

➢ Exhale as you release the tension and think the word 'relax'

➢ Imagine your foot sinking into the mat as you relax

➢ Notice the difference between tension and relaxation and repeat this tense/relax action for all the muscle groups in the following order:

1. Right foot - curl your toes downward and hold

2. Right lower leg and foot -pull your toes toward you

3. Entire right leg - squeeze thigh muscles together and hold

4. Repeat with the left leg

5. Right hand - clench your hand in a fist and hold

6. Entire right arm - tighten your biceps by drawing your forearm up toward your shoulder, keep clenching your fist, and hold

7. Repeat with the left arm

8. Buttocks - squeeze your buttocks together and hold

9. Stomach - pull in your stomach and hold

10. Chest - take a deep breath and hold

11. Neck and shoulders - shrug up your shoulders and hold

12. Face - screw up your face and hold

Playing soothing music and using an essential oil fragrance can enhance the experience. Practise this technique twice a day for two weeks. This will embed it into your psyche. As you become practised, you should be able to create a relax response by thinking of your keyword 'relax' (choose any keyword, just keep it the same).

As you get more confident try combining deep breathing with progressive muscle relaxation for additional stress relief.

Short Version of Progressive Muscle Relaxation

After you have been practising this for a few weeks, you can move toward a short version. Tense and relax larger muscle groups simultaneously. These muscle groups are:

➢ Lower limbs - feet and legs

➢ Stomach and chest

➢ Arms, shoulders, and neck

➢ Face

The next step is to practise 'release only'. Now that you know how relaxed muscles feel, you can simply deep breathe, start at your feet and slowly work up your body, releasing any tension.

Rhythmic Exercise

You might not think that exercising is relaxing. As mentioned earlier, it may be more beneficial if you have a 'flight response' to pressure. Rhythmic exercises - rowing, swimming, cycling, walking or jogging - with their repetitive action can have a calming effect. Practice mindfulness while exercising. Notice the rhythmic movements and how your body feels. Focus on the sensations of your feet or hands. Breathe in time with the rhythm of your exercise.

Power Yoga

With its dynamic poses and focus on fitness, power yoga is modelled on Ashtanga yoga. It strengthens your body, increases flexibility, and improves posture and balance. You're going to get sweaty so dress appropriately - and don't overdo it. We do not recommend attempting this type of yoga on your own.

Let's Sum Up

Stress is exhilarating - like the rush when bungee jumping.

Stress triggers a burst of energy to cope with danger.

Stress should not be confused with anxiety, they're different.

Take your time to adjust to new situations.

Stress is cumulative so understand the symptoms.

You can actively improve your tolerance levels to stress.

Understand your response to pressure - fight or flight?

Practise relaxation often, even if you aren't stressed.

What You Can Achieve

Use stress positively to help you perform.

Understand the stress response of others.

You get out of life what you put into it

~ Paul McQueen

CHAPTER EIGHT

Empowerment

Who Are You?

The Greek philosopher Aristotle thought the answer to this lay in our habits, 'We are what we repeatedly do'. Whereas, the German philosopher Martin Heidegger believed that who we are came from how we interact with the world and others. I think the latter is probably closer to how we understand it today.

Our deep-seated convictions of who we are form the context for our life. How we see ourselves, our self-view, influences our emotions and behaviour.

Unfortunately, hundreds of studies have shown that our self-view is rarely in line with our actual behaviour. Can we realistically be trusted to appraise ourselves objectively, given our ego? If that were possible, then our self-view would match what others say about us (our reputation). Studies prove that in the majority of cases, others don't see us the way we see ourselves. Mobster Al Capone saw himself as a folk hero. The bigger the gap between how people perceive you and how you view yourself, the greater the dysfunction in your relationships.

Others can make a more accurate assessment of who you are as they can observe your behaviour. So, if you want to know the answer, you only need to ask other people; although, when it comes to 'who we are' we don't like critical feedback. When was the last time you asked someone what they really thought of you? Do you think you got an honest answer? This is when people allow themselves little white lies to keep the peace.

Why Is It Important to Be Self-Aware?

Self-awareness is not only noticing your personal traits, it is also the ability to consciously monitor your emotions and thoughts. Being honest and non-judgemental with yourself as you gather information about your internal states, preferences, resources, and inhibitions is key to understanding yourself better. You are the sum of your beliefs, values, qualities, strengths, and weaknesses. Self-awareness is being able to manage your thoughts, emotions, and behaviour in line with those attributes.

Many of you may think that your self-view is simply built up from past experiences of places, events, and circumstances. However, it has more to do with the thoughts and beliefs that determine your experience of life. We discussed in the 'anxiety section' how emotions/feelings are stored in our brains after an experience, so you can act quickly should a similar event happen again. It's perceptions that decide whether an experience was good or bad. People going through the same experience feel quite different effects. You are responsible for the creation of your memories, whether good or bad. It is these memories (however twisted to suit your own purpose) that determine our self-view. You are who you think you are.

Self-awareness is being aware of the conditioning you encounter when creating these memories and controlling it.

Self-Awareness for Success

Researchers at Green Peak Partners and Cornell University studied 72 top executives at companies with revenues ranging from $50 million to $5 billion. They found that a high self-awareness score was the strongest predictor of overall success. The advantages are clear, executives who are aware of their weaknesses are often more prepared to hire subordinates who perform well in categories in which they lack acumen. Such leaders are also more able to entertain the idea that someone on their team may have an idea that is better than their own.

Know Thyself

How well do you know yourself? Do you know how others perceive you? Self-awareness is a rich and complicated subject, which is important for achieving success and happiness. The process of becoming self-aware may take a little time. Here is a start.

Get Honest Feedback

Do you see yourself as others do? Or do you have blind spots, certain traits that others see but you don't. Find someone you trust, who will give you an honest opinion, which may not be as easy as you think. Resist the urge to defend yourself and take their critique on board; remain open so you can learn from it.

Create Some Space for Yourself

Take some time out each day to reflect on your life. I'm sure you've come a long way already and know what your greatest achievement was and understand what went wrong in your life and why. Avoid blaming others for mishaps in your life, look to yourself first. Be brutally honest with yourself about what sort of a person you are.

There are many ways to approach this. Go for a walk, write notes in a journal, make use of your commuting time. Focus on the important things in your life and connect with yourself.

Practise Mindfulness Skills

Mindfulness has been described as paying attention in a particular way, on purpose, in the present moment, non-judgementally. It has been proven scientifically that it reduces levels of anxiety and stress, improves sleep quality, and positively changes how you feel about life experiences. You can work with trained teachers, but you can also learn these skills from self-help books.

Mindfulness is a very large subject, so you can read more on:

 hotlifestyle.info/life/mind

Self-awareness is important for understanding and developing good interpersonal skills. It is also the first step toward developing emotional intelligence.

Emotional Intelligence

If you want to manage your emotions and improve your relationships, then your EQ (Emotional Intelligence Quotient) matters. EQ is a measure of a person's emotional intelligence that was created by psychologist Daniel Goleman whose book sold over 5,000,000 copies. It looks at the role emotional intelligence plays in excellence through four key competencies:

Self-Awareness

Through which you know your strengths and weaknesses and can acknowledge the effect your emotions (anger, sadness, fear, etc.) have on your thoughts and behaviour.

Self-Management

So that you remain calm and in control of your emotions and behaviours in stressful situations. You take the initiative and move toward your goals.

Social Awareness - Empathy

When you recognize and interpret the emotions, needs, and concerns of others, which allows you to communicate with them in a way that they can understand.

Relationship Skills

Enable you to communicate in a clear, persuasive manner. They make you a team player who can build relationships and manage conflict.

Understanding and using emotional intelligence in your daily life changes your perspective. More reading on this fascinating subject can be found on:

 hotlifestyle.info/life/EQ

Borrowed Genius

Borrowed genius, is a powerful, accelerated learning technique developed by Dr. Win Wenger, PhD, a pioneer in the fields of creativity and creative method, accelerated learning, and brain and mind development. It was first created in the 1960s by Professor Vladimir Raikov from Moscow and was called the ‚Raikov Effect'. I have seen different versions of this technique in many books but have never seen a credit to the originator whose work was quite extraordinary.

Dr. Wenger enrolled his 4-year-old daughter in the local swimming team. An administrative error had her competing with a group of kids twice her age. To Wenger's amazement she swam fast enough to finish in the middle of the pack. When asked how she's managed it, she replied, 'I made believe that I was one of the big kids'. From this, came the spark for what has become known as 'borrowed genius'.

Children learn by pretending but, as we grow older, we tend to forget this skill or view it as being childish. This tried and tested accelerated learning technique can be used for developing a special skill or for improving creativity. It helps you adopt the mindset of someone else, even somebody you've never met.

By stepping into the 'skin' of the person you want to model you take on their traits. After you step out of that skin, the learned skills remain with you.

Will This Technique Work For Every Occasion?

It has been proven to help you learn faster, on condition you have a basic skill set to build upon. If you have no musical talent, haven't had any musical training, have never played an instrument, or have no interest in music then using this technique to play guitar like Brian May will not work. The knowledge base is simply not there upon which you can build. On the other hand, let's say you like to cook, have a good basic knowledge, and had some basic training, then modelling Jamie Oliver, who you have probably seen on television, would give you a distinct advantage. During official studies, where certain criteria by the candidates was already met, then improvements have been seen in a space of ten minutes, although this is not the norm. Most people need to practise for 5-6 weeks in three or more sessions per week. The more effort you put in, the more you get out of it. Try it out, with a little patience you will see a result.

The best conditions for using this technique are that:

➢ you have a sound knowledge of the subject matter

➢ you know the person you want to model quite well

➢ the issue is a minor one, bigger skill sets take longer

Let's run through the process for someone who would like more confidence.

The Process of Borrowed Genius

Decide what you want to learn or the problem you want to solve and write it down. It can be used for developing skills, learning, inventing, writing, solving problems, confidence ...

Decide who you want to model. Who do you know that is confident? A television personality, a politician or someone you work with. Remember, the closer you are to this person the better the outcome. Write down the name of your chosen genius - how about Bill or Hilary Clinton?

Find a quiet place and make yourself comfortable. Use a deep relaxation technique to create a state of complete relaxation. When you're completely relaxed.

Picture yourself standing in the most beautiful garden you've ever seen. Make it lush and colourful, with flowerbeds, trees, birds. Look around and notice what you see, hear, and smell. Make it feel real.

After a while you're joined in the garden by the person you have chosen to model. Have them walk toward you smiling and greeting you. Visualize the person standing in front of you and make them real. Describe their clothes, shoes, note as much detail as possible. Feel their warm, welcoming personality - they are obviously glad to see you.

The genius then turns their back to you, allowing you to step into their body. Move forward and, as you would put on a suit, step inside the genius. See the world through their eyes, hear through their ears, feel what they feel. Look around the garden again and notice how they perceive it. Are there any differences? Notice their posture, how they walk, their mannerisms, and how they feel and think.

What do you want to learn from your genius? You can move to a completely different place where you can practise the required skill. I would go to the Oval Office and sit behind that beautiful desk. What confident posture have you taken up. Feel the respect you get from others and feel how good it is. If you have a particular issue with, say, making phone calls, then while you're here make a call and make a presentation to someone on the products you work with. Notice how you are sitting when calling, note the hand gestures. Where are you looking? Out of the window? Use this opportunity to address real life issues that you have. If you have a pending presentation coming up, practise it on White House staff. Notice how Bill/Hillary deals with it. The key here is to notice how your genius feels when they are doing the activity you want to learn. Notice in particular their posture, hand gestures, sounds, and facial expressions. Are their eyes open or closed?

Since you have the memories of this genius, go and find the moment of greatest understanding in their lifetime - the time when everything came together. Find that 'aha!' moment and describe it in detail - the experience itself and then the perceptions and understandings that came out of it.

When you're ready to finish. Walk in front of a full-length mirror. See the genius in the mirror and with one clap of your hands the mirror has gone leaving the genius in front of you and you standing there facing them. Show your gratitude and smile as you give thanks for the opportunity. Let your genius explain a key point or something important about the experience. Take the time to listen to what they have to say. Now have your genius give you a mobile telephone as a gesture that you can contact them at any time in the future. See them pocketing their own phone. This technique seems to work better when there are reciprocal feelings, so let there be an understanding that your genius can also contact you at any time.

Start counting backward from 10, 9, 8, … with each number you start to return to yourself. When you reach one you are fully awake and refreshed. Write what happened in a journal. Try to include as much detail as possible about body posture, gestures, skills passed on to you. Write in the present tense. Note the differences between your view of the garden and that of your genius. Practise your new-found skill within 12 hours of a session. Over the next seven days, you should work with your genius at least once a day.

Confidence

I remember the very first sales course I attended at the age of eighteen. The one thing that got my attention was:

Your success will be determined by how
well you perform under pressure.

We all know about pressure and the responses we can have to it. Instead of an emotional response people with confidence stop for a second, and have a more considered response.

At the core of confidence is an unwavering belief in yourself. It's the ability to get over your fears and try new things, leave your comfort zone and, should you fail, get up again, change direction, and stay with it. It's not the person who talks most in meetings or sits in the front row at seminars. Confidence is a quality that can be associated with the person who takes action and can perform when under pressure. The more often you take action, the easier it gets. Failure is simply part of the process. If you have never failed, then you have never done anything!

 hotlifestyle.info/fail

I have not failed 1,000 times. I have successfully
discovered 1,000 ways to NOT make a light bulb

~ Thomas Edison

Be in the present. Mindfulness is all about being here and now. As soon as your mind wanders to your appearance or how you're feeling today, then you will lose the connection with your train of thought, risk going blank and losing your confidence. The key to mindfulness and living in the present moment is to practise every day. Confident people are 100% engaged in the present moment. Whether you're on the telephone or in a meeting stay focused and in the present.

 hotlifestyle.info/life/mind

Take ownership, regardless of what it is, stand behind it 100%. Whether it's your beliefs and opinions, or your ideas to help your company. Be authentic to your self; if you can't stand 100% behind something then don't do it. I remember being told that the art of public speaking was simply to talk on a subject that you passionately believe in. It's time to stop apologizing for who you are and own it.

Take action. This is key to building confidence. Each day, take a deliberate step out of your comfort zone, no matter how small. If talking to someone that you find attractive is an issue, then take one small step and smile at someone you find attractive. You may want to practise first before attempting to talk to the person of your desire. Only by practising daily can you desensitize yourself.

NLP (Neuro Linguistic Programming)

NLP, in my opinion, is one of the most important lifeskills. It was created in the 1970s by Richard Bandler and John Grinder. They believed that if you modelled the thoughts and behaviours of successful individuals then you would achieve similar results. Practising NLP will help you manage your thoughts and feelings, regardless of external factors that may affect you. Although the principles are easy, it can take a little time to master. After a while though, you don't consciously notice how NLP influences your decision making.

The principles of NLP can be applied in both business and private environments. It can help you with personal development and gives you the tools to undergo painless, fast change. It can be used to improve your life, health, relationships, income, career, and more.

The intention of this book is to introduce you to evidence-based, tried and tested principles for achieving a Hotlifestyle. There are courses you can attend but, in my opinion, you can learn this technique from reading about it. We have already broached some NLP techniques in this book.

To understand NLP further and embark on your journey of change visit:

 hotlifestyle.info/NLP

Setting Goals

Just the action of setting goals and listing your aspirations can be very motivating. It allows you to set targets to aim for. But, a goal without a plan is simply a wish. Create a realistic plan designating a time frame by which you want certain things to be in place. Then step by step take action on that plan.
Read more about setting goals on:

 hotlifestyle.info/life/SG

Let's Sum Up

Empowerment is about confidence and controlling your life.

Become self-aware and understand how others see you.

Practice the four key skills for emotional intelligence.

Techniques like borrowed genius will help you learn faster.

Build confidence by taking a small action every day.

Mastering NLP is one of the most important skill sets.

Setting clear goals will give you direction in life.

What You Can Achieve

More confidence every time you step further into the water.
A new dimension for learning using borrowed genius.

*Simply by paying attention
you create a memory*

~ Paul McQueen

CHAPTER NINE

Memory

Something Memorable

So, where did you leave your keys? Have you ever driven to work and couldn't remember how you actually got there? Not to worry, if there had been an incident you would have reacted OK. For half our lives we run on automatic, and there's no memory technique that will help you remember trivial information like where you left your keys, because our short-term memory is 'short' and easily distracted, and you have other priorities when you get home. How about putting your keys in the same place each time? It's the only sure-fire method for knowing where your keys will be.

The Mechanics of Memory

Ten people see the same incident, each will have noticed different things about it, each will have a different memory of the event. We don't all see the same thing, and our life experiences and personalities can create a biased view as the memory is formed. Memory is often more interpretive than factual. We won't delve into the problems of witnesses recall and their unreliability in court. What we do want to emphasize is that what you retain from your experiences, and how you perceive them, can have a profound effect on your happiness. It's not the experience that counts, it's what you remember about it that resonates strongly. To go deeper into this subject visit:

 hotlifestyle.info/life/EVM

Memory can be defined in two ways:

1. by how long the memories last

2. what the memories are for

There are three types of memory when defined by how long memories last:

Immediate (Sensory) Memory

These give us continuity and we're not really aware of them. They last a millisecond and join up the pictures like a movie. You see a car in the distance which drives past you and heads off. The scene makes sense because you had the memory of where the car started and where it ended.

Short-Term (Working) Memory

This is the information we are thinking about in the present. These 'now' memories stay around long enough to be helpful for what you're doing. They're only stored for about 20-30 seconds and come from paying attention to sensory memories - starting the car, meeting someone new and hearing their name, laying your keys down. You forget most of these memories very shortly after the event has happened, and it doesn't matter.

Long-Term Memory

These memories can last from an hour to a lifetime. The mechanism that transfers short-term storage into long-term memories is still not well understood. What we do know is that repeating something over and over again will commit it to long-term memory. ‚Chunking', taking smaller bits of information and combining them for more meaning and association, commits the whole to long-term memory.

Defining memory by what they are for, has two scenarios:

A Memory of WHAT Something Is

We can easily describe these memories, which would include such things as what your job is or where you went on holiday.

A Memory of HOW Something Is Done

We cannot describe these memories, which cover such skills as how to play the guitar, how to bake, or how to sail.

Factors That Can Affect Memory

Fitness, nutrition, and quality sleep will all affect your memory. Researchers at Northumbria University found that smoking had a negative influence on memory. A group of students aged between 18 and 25 were split into smokers who averaged 60 cigarettes per week and non-smokers. They were asked to memorize a list of tasks. The non-smokers were able to complete 81% of the tasks, the smokers only 59%. A similar result was obtained from King's College London in a separate study.

US researchers from the journal Neurology, monitored the diets of 17,478 people whose average age was 64. They found that people who followed a Mediterranean diet were 19% less likely to develop memory problems and also had a reduced risk of dementia.

 hotlifestyle.info/vit/med

What's Their Name?

The ability to remember names and faces, especially when under pressure, is key to your success. Being able to remember somebody's name is particularly important, as calling someone by their name will get their immediate attention and help create a rapport. There are a few methods to help you remember people's names. Depending on whether your learning style is visual, auditory, or kinaesthetic (movement/touch), you could try one of the following.

Association (Visual)

Picture something relating to their name and see it on their face as you hear it, or see their name written across their forehead. The more bizarre the association the more memorable it will be - if you meet someone called Roger imagine a rabbit running around his head. Be creative in your visualization.

Rhyming (Auditory)

Get creative and make up a rhyme of their name and something that relates to them. The key here is that the rhyme relates to the person and that it pops up spontaneously when you meet them. Can you make a link to someone's physical attribute, business, hobby, or location? You're never going to say this out loud, so make it as bizarre as you like - tall Paul, Gayle sails, red Ted, and so on.

Shout it Out Loud in Your Head (Auditory)

Create a habit of shouting their name out loud in your head several times while looking at their face. Then try and use their name casually in the conversation or, better still, mention it to someone else directly after the conversation, for instance, 'I just met John Doe, have you seen his car?'

Write it With Your Finger (Kinaesthetic)

As you hear their name, imagine writing it with your finger. If you slightly move your finger in tune with this imagery you will embed their name into your neurology.

Use of Anchors

Think of how, during his candidacy, President Trump placed ,anchors' in the minds of voters with the phrases Crooked Hillary, Cheatin' Obama, Little Marco, and so on. As you read each name, you know straight away who's being referred to. In addition, he has attached a negative feeling to each name. So, if you want someone to remember your name, then when you introduce yourself, associate it with a positive anchor. Example, 'Hi, I'm Paul with the drinks.'

If you practise one of these techniques with everyone you meet, it will soon become second nature and you'll do it subconsciously whenever you meet someone new. The key here is - practice, practice, practice.

The Stuff Memories Are Made Of

We all agree that it is important to improve our own memory. It is just as important that other people remember points we want to get across. There are several ways in which memories are formed in ourselves and others.

Memories Formed Through Location/Story Association

We form and recall memories through making associations. We have already seen examples of this above. Memories can be intrinsically tied to a location. Do you remember where you were when you heard the news about Lady Diana? Millions of years ago our survival depended on remembering which place was dangerous, how to find our way back to camp, where the food was, and so on. The association with location is so strong in us that it is used as the basis of a memory technique. The method of loci, also known as the memory palace, associates things to be remembered with objects you are familiar with as you visualize them together walking around a palace.

Memories Formed Through Emotional Association

We have already discussed how emotions are added to an event. Memories tied to emotions are probably the strongest memories we have. So much so, that if you recall a memory associated with a strong emotional state, you feel the state anew.

Memories Formed Through Repetition

However boring this may sound, it has been used by schools around the world for many years. Even if you're using the memory palace technique, you have to knuckle down in the beginning and repeatedly go through the palace to remember the specific items you will attach things to. Remember, it's not practice that makes perfect. It's perfect practice that makes perfect.

Memories Recalled Like Links On A Chain

To reach a specific memory, you generally go through a host of others. The brain tends to group similar concepts and terms in clusters. You can use this to your advantage when studying, by not jumping around different subjects too much you'll help to build clusters.

THE CRUX OF IT

If you want others to remember what you say, then associate your message with a feeling, a place, or an emotion. To reinforce the memory, make sure you repeat your point a few times in different ways, maybe tie it to a story, an illustration or an anecdote. Keep it simple, so your audience doesn't have to access their long-term memory to grasp it.

Supplements

As with all supplements, read the instructions on dosage and side effects. If your aim is memory improvement, then don't just take any brain supplement. Choose only those that contain ingredients proven to boost memory. As we are all different, look for the effects of a particular supplement to see what works for you. We always recommend consulting a nutritionist before starting supplementation of any sort.

Acetyl-l-Carnitine
Not to be confused with the less expensive version named simply ‚l-Carnitine'. Acetyl-l-Carnitine (ALC) is an amino acid whose ability to improve memory problems in the elderly or from excessive alcohol use is well documented.

Brahmi (Bacopa Monnieri)
Brahmi is a plant from India used in traditional Ayurveda medicine. Don't confuse it with Gotu Kola, which is also sometimes called Brahmi but is not the same thing. Research has shown that taking the herb Bacopa increases production of the neurotransmitter acetylcholine, which improves memory in older adults. It also increases resilience to mental and physical stress by balancing the neurotransmitters dopamine, serotonin, and GABA.

Ginkgo
Ginkgo biloba is one of the most popular herbal remedies around and should be considered if you're studying a lot. It can significantly improve blood circulation, especially through the

smallest blood vessels (capillaries), and increases the level of oxygen and nutrients in brain tissues.

Omega-3 Essential Fatty Acids

Fish oil has a proven track record of improving brain functions of all kinds, including memory, mood, mental wellbeing. If you take it in a capsule there's no aftertaste.

Phosphatidylserine

It helps boost memory and learning and helps prevent age-related mental decline. It is found naturally in meat and fish and in small amounts in dairy products and vegetables.

Nootropics

Nootropics, or smart drugs, are supplements that boost mental functions such as focus, memory, and attention span.

 hotlifestyle.info/NT

Scientists are making some interesting discoveries on healthy brain foods to help boost concentration and focus when eaten regularly. Further reading can be found on:

 hotlifestyle.info/vit/CF

Setting the Anchor

Anchoring is a very powerful tool used in NLP to associate a trigger with an emotion/state or to induce a certain frame of mind. Bandler and Grinder define it as: 'Anchoring refers to the tendency for any one element of an experience (trigger/ memory could be visual, auditory, smell or kinaesthetic) to bring back the entire experience'.

We're actually doing this all of the time, but most of us are not consciously aware of it. Some examples of things you have anchored unconsciously would be the song (auditory) you shared with your first love. I bet you still remember it, and when you hear it, you think of them, and reach a specific state.

The smell from a big brewery always reminds me of a specific time in my childhood. So, thinking of an experience from a long time ago, I had set an anchor and can change my state years later when it is triggered. It makes sense to deliberately set anchors to change your, or someone else's, state at will. This is especially useful when you need peak performance.

Setting anchors to make changes to your, or someone else's, state is easy, and the effect is immediate.

 hotlifestyle.info/life/anchor

Harnessing Total Recall

Go Through the Alphabet

Struggling to remember the characters' names in Ice Age? Picture the sloth in your mind and go through the alphabet starting with 'A' to find the first letter of his name. Doing this exercise will jog your memory.

Chunking

When you have to remember a telephone number or a date, turn them into memorable chunks and add some sense that will help you remember it. To remember the numbers 9-1-1 think 911 Porsche, which is easier than remembering each number. You can extend this to make a series of words, for instance, 9111066, becomes 'A Porsche went to the Battle of Hastings'.

Memory Palace

Have you seen the whizz kids on TV memorizing a pack of playing cards or committing 6,270 binary numbers to memory in just 30 minutes? (See Munkhshur Narmandakh from Mongolia in 2017.) Memory champions around the globe use the memory palace technique for what seems like magic to most of us. Those who use it say that anyone can learn it.

 hotlifestyle.info/life/cards

Write a To-Do List Each Day

Taking time out to write a to-do list allows you to think of all the things you have to get done, then tick off items as you do them. At the days end, you can see how much you got done.

Use Flash Cards

This is a great mnemonic device if you have to learn a lot of facts, like dates in history or a second language. This technique will have you knowing your subject backward and forward. There are many apps online that offer flash cards covering many subjects, but I recommend that you make your own cards as the action of writing them yourself makes it much easier for you to remember. Let's use the example of learning a second language, say German. Write the German word on one side of your card and a brief definition (you could also include a simple drawing) on the other side. When you have about 50 cards use the spaced repetition technique to begin learning.

Look at the German word and answer with the definition that should be on the reverse side of the card. Build two piles of cards, those you answered correctly and those you did not know. Take a ‚Pomodoro' break of around five minutes then go through the pile of cards that you did not know. Do this three or four times, taking a short break between each exercise. The next day look at the definition side and answer with the German word, placing the don't knows in a separate pile. Take a break and use the same technique to end up with a small pile of cards that you don't know the answer to. This is a great way to find out what you don't know and what you need to brush up on.

 hotlifestyle.info/life/FC

Memory Courses

There are many accredited courses to help you learn memory techniques.

Does Brain Jogging Improve Memory?

This has been a huge trend over the past few years, with a new app popping up each week. They all work on the premise that if you use your brain enough, you can slow down its deterioration and help improve your memory. According to Dr. William Kormos, editor in chief of Harvard Men's Health Watch, early studies concentrated on people with healthy habits who were a low-risk group. Much research is flawed as there is often no comparison group or no follow-up to measure decline. The largest and longest study combined exercise and diet with brain training, making it impossible to determine if any one factor contributed to improved memory. The evidence is inconclusive and only if you really enjoy doing crosswords or sudoku should you do it. Admittedly, the more you do, the better you will become.

Let's Sum Up

A memory of an event can differ between individuals.

Fitness and wellbeing play an important role in memory.

Follow a Mediterranean diet and take regular exercise.

Use techniques for remembering someone's name.

Consider using supplements for improving memory.

Sleep is important for building long-term memory.

There are ways to help others remember your message.

Anchoring is a powerful NLP tool for changing states.

Mnemonic devices are helpful tools to improve memory.

Brain jogging doesn't boost memory but can be fun.

What You Can Achieve

Memory techniques for better grades in exams.

Rapport is easier if you can remember things about others.

Help people remember your words for a bigger impact.

At the point of no return
when self-defence becomes the final option,
know what you're doing

~ Paul McQueen

CHAPTER TEN

Self-Defence

The Reality of Self-Defence

Lack of inhibition and a willingness to commit violence
without thinking make the world a dangerous place. Some
500,000 people worldwide die each year as a result of street
violence. This means about 1,400 people are killed each day.
Add to this the 30,000-50,000 hospitalized each day due to
the severity of their violence-related injuries and there is cause
for concern. It is reckoned that one in five of us will have a
violent confrontation at some time, and the situation is getting
worse. Such confrontations can have devastating, long-lasting
consequences for the victim. Don't become a victim!

The first form of defence should be observational psychology and pre-incident indicators. Body language will tell you a lot about someone's intentions. Being aware of your surroundings will help you avoid a potential confrontation by keeping it at a distance. Walking through a gang on the street simply taunts them to a point that (and there is always one) they have to prove themselves. Criminals and bullies look for easy prey and tend to use the element of surprise, strength in numbers, distraction, or false pretence to initiate their attack, so you'll be at the point of no return as soon as the incident starts, leaving you with no chance of avoiding it.

As it is an offence in many countries to carry any form of weapon for protection, you should consider what course of action to take if you are attacked. When push comes to shove, you should have the ability to defend yourself and your loved ones. It's a necessary skill that you'd rather not put into practice but learning even basic self-defence gives you power and improves your chances of escaping unscathed.

The first thing you will have to overcome is the fight or flight mechanism built into all of us. Jelly-knees are normal. Learning any combat sport is going to help you deal with the fight or flight mechanism.

If you are inclined to learn a martial art, then Muay Thai Boxing, also known as kickboxing, is the one I would recommend. Muay Thai is the national sport of Thailand that developed from a form of hand-to-hand close combat. It's been around for hundreds of years and continues to grow in popularity all around the world. Unlike other combat sports you use your whole body, making it a full body workout like no other. It's relatively simple to learn and is a physically intense system of combat. It is also highly effective for weight loss, increasing cardiovascular fitness and endurance, and building confidence and control in difficult situations. You will gain a lot from learning a martial art form like Muay Thai, but it might not be the best method for defending yourself on the street.

I personally don't want to learn a martial art with lots of moves and techniques. I have no interest in spending years on formal self-defence classes for a black belt or to take part in competitions. What I do want is the ability to defend myself and my loved ones fast and effectively.

If you simply want to defend yourself with minimum risk of injury, then Krav Maga is the obvious choice. It targets vital points that neutralize your opponent, with an emphasis on saving your life by attacking before being attacked. It will also teach you how to neutralize armed attackers, which is not considered at all in Muay Thai. Muay Thai is structured on rounds of fighting with fixed rules and a referee, whereas Krav Maga has no fixed rules and is not a competition sport. From a self-defence point of view, both have their merits, which is why some people consider learning both techniques.

Regardless of the technique you decide on, being fit is paramount to any success when protecting yourself. Being fitter than your opponent will give you the competitive edge in any confrontation both physically and psychologically. If your opponent sees that you are fitter than them it may even de-escalate the situation. Bullies want an easy victim.

Krav Maga

After the defeat at Dunkirk during World War II, it was considered how best to train thousands of troops, in the shortest possible time, in an effective defence technique. Former Royal Marine William E. Fairbairn had developed and refined a close quarters combat system which originated during his time in Shanghai, teaching their police force. He was enlisted into the secret service to teach his method to American, Canadian, and British troops. This highly effective technique could be learned with only a few days training and minimal skill, it was known as The Shanghai Method. As time went on the method was improved and acquired different names, such as Defendu, reality self-defence. Close combat training (USA) or close quarter combat (CQC) as we say in the UK is the basis of Krav Maga (Hebrew for contact combat), which was adopted by Mossad, the Israeli Police, and many other forces around the globe. This is the method I would most recommend if your aim is to defend yourself on the street.

There are courses countrywide. It is not recommended that you learn it out of a book. Apart from being a great workout, I like this form of self-defence because the aim is to end the fight as soon as possible by causing maximum damage to your opponent. This sounds like a good plan to use against anyone who wants to harm me.

When Dogs Attack

Dog attacks are on the rise, despite the control of certain breeds. Your chances of being bitten by a dog in the United States is about 1 in 72, that works out to around 4.5 million dog bites per year, compared to about 200,000 attacks per year in the UK. As such attacks can be fatal I thought it should be included here. When dogs attack, it's usually because they either feel threatened or you have moved into their territory. If you are moving faster than walking pace, you trigger a dog's natural instinct to hunt, and it will give chase.

For further reading:

 hotlifestyle.info/life/DA

Confrontation - What Usually Happens

You will notice that there are no diagrams or specific explanations of moves to defend yourself noted here. I didn't want to give you a false sense of security. Simply reading about defence techniques is not going to save you if you find yourself in a bad situation. The facts are that there is no standard situation and we can't say what usually happens as each scenario is different. There is no substitute for taking classes. Place the key words Krav Maga together with your nearest town into a search engine to find classes near you.

Let's Sum Up

There is no winner in violent confrontation.

Avoid direct confrontation and observe body language.

Don't think you can watch videos and protect yourself.

Take lessons in self-defence from an approved school.

Make sure you are fit enough before taking lessons.

Muay Thai Boxing, or kickboxing, is taught in many places.

Krav Maga, is taught in many places.

Have a strategy to deal with aggressive dogs.

What You Can Achieve

The ability to defend yourself will boost your confidence.

Meet new people taking lessons and improve your fitness.

It just may save your life one day.

Final Thoughts on Lifeskills

We have looked at personal traits in some detail, what discoveries did you make about yourself?

First encounters are the beginning for long relationships and dealing with them effectively is very important. You see now why anxiety and stress was included. The effect these two factors have on your personality will determine, to some degree, your success in life. Building on your portfolio of lifeskills will help you gain confidence. That is what this book has been all about. As cited right at the start, 'competence builds confidence'. Confidence in itself is a funny concept. There is no class to teach you confidence, it comes from stepping a little further into the water each day, feeling more and more at ease with situations or encounters. It's really about overcoming your fears and taking action. Easier said than done for some of you, I know. It really does begin with the first step and noting how well you master the situation. Just don't give up, try to instigate situations so you can practise. When the big one comes along, and your performance really matters, make sure you're ready to face the challenge. The basic tools are all here to help you gain strength for your success.

Find out what gives you strength, and courage will follow.

BOOK THREE

INTERACTIONS

Do Unto Others as You
Would Have Them Do to You

INTRODUCTION

We partake in social intercourse on a daily basis, but have we mastered it? Our ability to interact with others by talking openly and listening, decides the quality of our relationships. A good communication style is the basis for successful interactions and is essential for building strong, lasting relationships.

It's obvious that having people skills is important, but how can we use them effectively in our day to day lives? The most common cause of miscommunication is sending mixed signals. Do your non-verbal cues - your facial expressions and body language - correspond with what you're actually saying?

Positive psychologist Chris Peterson, a professor at the University of Michigan, says the best advice to come out of his field is to make strong personal relationships your priority. Good relationships are buffers against the damaging effects of life's inevitable let-downs and setbacks.

*Happiness depends on
who you choose to spend time with.*

Your ability to interact easily and to connect with others will influence your Hotlifestyle.

Because people can't read your mind,
you're going to have to talk to them

~ Paul McQueen

CHAPTER ELEVEN

Communication

The Art of Good Communication

To get on in this world, it's important to get your point across, solve conflict, tell someone how you are feeling or what your needs are, and much more. Most importantly, you should connect with others to build strong relationships. All of which is achieved by using clear, concise communication. But, if you simply steamroller someone with your ideas, however nicely, you will not win them over. Good communication is a two-way street. When you have something important to say to someone, don't use the telephone. Phones convey only 15% of your message and leave it open to misinterpretation by watering it down.

Important conversations should only take place face to face. Here are some pointers for when you have to communicate something really important:

➢ Check that your appearance is appropriate

➢ Ensure there will be no interruptions
  or distractions from phones, TV, and so on

➢ Know what you want to say,
  and the result you want to achieve

➢ Make sure the message is understood

➢ Watch your tone of voice

➢ Show empathy and listen carefully
  to what they have to say

➢ Give some merit to their point of view

➢ Stay positive, do not condemn,
  and try to understand them

➢ Discuss your point of view and
  stay calm and focused

Non-Verbal Communication

While 30% of your message is communicated by your tone of voice, (There is some truth in the phrase 'It's not what you say, it's how you say it'.) 60% is communicated non-verbally, which means that only 10% is communicated by what you actually say (the content). Actions really do speak louder than words.

Non-verbal communication conveys empathy and emotion through gestures, expressions, and body language. As these are less easy to fake than words, people tend to rely on them for understanding what you are saying. Non-verbal communication conveys happiness, anger, sadness, interest, curiosity, hurt, annoyance, embarrassment, anxiety, pleasure, hope, and so on - emotions that people show unconsciously most of the time. If what you're saying is not congruent with your non-verbal cues, then you will not be credible, and the non-verbal cues take precedence and are believed.

Observing non-verbal cues will tell you what the other party is thinking as you're talking to them. Important signals to look for when talking to somebody are things like disinterest, are they doodling on a piece of paper or glancing at their watch?

Negative body language like rolling of eyes or folded arms can tell you to change your tack. Observe a positive change in their posture like them leaning forward or unfolding their arms means that you are probably getting your message across.

How Non-Verbal Cues can be Used

Repetition can support your message by being in alignment (congruent) with what you are saying.

Contradiction can confuse your verbal message. For instance, by nodding in agreement while saying ,no' or shaking your head from side to side while saying 'yes'.

Substitution can be used in place of a verbal message. An eyebrow raised in surprise can often convey more than words.

Complementing may enhance a verbal message. Patting someone on the back while praising a job well done enhances the impact of your message.

Accenting may be used to underline a verbal message. Pounding the table with your fist will certainly drive your point across.

What Your Tone Of Voice Is Saying

Vocal tones influence the way your message is received. We have all used sarcasm to get a point across at some time, for example. The volume, rhythm, and inflection of your voice (sincerity, jocularity, sarcasm) give the listener an insight to the true meaning of your message and are just as powerful as the words you use. It is important to practise this technique, especially if you use the telephone a lot. Try talking a little slower than usual for a day, learn to control HOW you say things.

Facial Expressions

The influential French artist Charles Le Brun (1619-1690) observed that all emotions affect the muscles of the face, and that the eyebrows in particular give a precise expression to our feelings. Our eyes (the window to our soul) are the most important tool for communicating feelings. The way someone looks at you will be very different when they feel affection, rage, guilt, or disgust.

Facial expressions are the same in cultures all over the world, whether for sadness, happiness, surprise, fear, or anger. They are hard to fake and are believed over any words. Read your listener's facial expressions for feedback on how they are receiving your message.

Eye Contact

Making eye contact is so important when you talk to anyone. A lack of eye contact gives the impression that you're either not honest or have something to hide. Too much eye contact can be weird and make people feel uncomfortable. When you walk through customs, they are looking to see how much eye contact you make with officers as an indication of whether they should search your bags.

Touch

The use of touch as a method of communication varies between cultures. The most common form is the handshake and a firm handshake is associated with strength of personality. You know yourself that receiving a handshake that is like a piece of limp lettuce, leaves a bad impression. Not everybody appreciates being touched, for example, if you take hold of a person's arm they might find it intimidating.

Personal Space

Encroaching on someone's personal space can make them feel threatened or anxious; it's an instinctive reaction when a stranger comes to close. Most people will tolerate an infringement on their intimate space on crowded buses, in lifts, at concerts, and so on. But most people's personal space is about 1.5 feet/0.5 metres around them. It does differ from person to person, relationship to relationship, and is not connected to how much they like you. Our preferences form at 3-4 years old and are pretty much ingrained in us by our teens. Be aware of someone's personal space and avoid getting too close, especially at first meetings.

Posture

Simply observing posture and stance will tell you immediately if someone is feeling confident or nervous. Holding your head up, walking with purpose and confidence sends a different message to slouching, eyes looking at the floor. In a one-to-one meeting posture communicates a wealth of information. Watch how they sit, are arms or legs crossed? Be aware of your own posture, what message do you want to send?

It's amazing how the slightest body movement is taken on board. They can be a distraction and they can give feedback on what someone is thinking during a conversation. In some cultures, as in Italy, gestures are a language in their own right. You use pointing or beckoning gestures all the time without being aware of them. Watch your body movements.

THE CRUX OF IT

Understanding your effect on others and how you interact in a non-verbal context is a complex subject. Verbal and non-verbal cues should work together in harmony in a subtle way. Be aware of your non-verbal cues and use those you observe as feedback on whether you are being agreed with or not.

Remember, only 10% of your message is put across with actual words. But, if you say the wrong thing during a job interview, there is no non-verbal cue that will save you.

The Power of Listening

Here's the thing. No one is interested in what you have to say. They are really only interested in themselves, things that interest them, and what they have to say. To understand what another person wants - whether it is your lover, your boss, or a complete stranger - you have to make a concerted effort to listen with empathy and understanding. If they don't feel that you have heard them out, then you have no chance of putting your point across effectively. Encouraging others to talk openly and honestly will get you to a win-win solution much more quickly.

Listening is an intricate part of the communication process and its importance should not be underestimated.

Regardless of who you're dealing with you should:

➢ Sit or stand facing them, not side on

➢ Ensure your eyes are physically on the same level

➢ Gestures should show your genuine interest and concern

➢ Leaning forward slightly can emphasise your concern

➢ Look relaxed, keep your arms and legs uncrossed

➢ Make eye contact but don't make it uncomfortable

➢ Avoid distractions, like fidgeting or feet/finger tapping

➢ Hear them out, without interruption

➢ If you get angry, break it off and take some time out

Communication With Loved Ones

The art of being a good listener is especially important when communicating with loved ones. Listening is not the same as hearing. It's about paying full attention to the other person's emotions, body language, and facial expressions. It's about showing empathy and understanding without being judgemental. Most relationships break down because people stop listening to one another and concentrate on their own agenda. Unlike communicating in the workplace or in public you are generally talking about more intimate and emotional topics, which can be harder to deal with, even embarrassing.

The hardest discussions in a relationship that you care about, and want to continue long term, are dealing with conflict; they require a great deal of diplomacy and tact.

Bear in mind the following:

➢ Clarify the motives for actions, don't speculate
➢ Keep dialogue open and avoid the silent treatment
➢ Get hold of the facts and don't judge
➢ Talk only in the present and future tenses
➢ Leave out the petty stuff, focus on the real problem
➢ Use 'I feel' rather than 'You are' statements
➢ We cover this subject in greater depth in
   People Sklls, chapter 12

Digital Communication

There's no getting away from the fact that much of our communication will be through a digital medium, such as email, SMS, or social media. We talk to each other quite differently using the electronic written word. We are abrupt, rude, quick to judge, and generally not very nice to deal with. But remember this simple fact, regardless of the medium you are dealing with another human being with feelings. For example, dumping someone with an SMS is pretty mean. Sexting on the other hand could land you in trouble should it go viral.

If people were to follow internet etiquette called 'Netiquette' it would certainly make reading on forums and other networks much more pleasant.

 hotlifestyle.info/int/SX

Every time you communicate through social media a note is made on your digital footprint. The digital world is not a private space, in fact, messages are stored for at least three months. People don't realize this and slander others, thinking they are anonymous. There is even a name for it. Internet 'trolls' are people who go out of their way to start a quarrel in a social group simply to create a reaction. Do you remember Brenda Leyland?

 hotlifestyle.info/int/net

Social Media - What's It Really Good For?

Who has an account on a social media platform? Better still, who doesn't have an account?

The companies made no secret of the fact that access to their services was on condition you received advertisements. It's just like television, you watch a movie on condition that every 20 minutes you allow advertisers into your home. You're trading their use/sale of your details so you can enjoy a 'free' service. Nothing is 'free'. Even when you're asked to give your mobile number to help you get back into your account should you be locked out, it means they have another useful piece of data to sell.

When social media began, teams were set up to think of ways to 'engage' users and have them stay longer on the platform. You could say they were looking for ways to get you addicted. Has it worked?

I check my social media once or twice a week and spend around ten minutes on it. Statistics say that, on average, we spend two hours per day on social media, and that this figure is rising, across all age groups.

'Big Brother' happened and we did it to ourselves! It's here to stay and has redefined the word 'friend'. Social media should serve you and not the other way around. Try spending one week without it. The world still goes on!

Professional Interactions

The more formal environment of the workplace requires a different behaviour to that with your family and friends. The workplace dress code might be casual but the way you communicate should not.

Always communicate in a professional manner when dealing with work colleagues and superiors. Sending emails with links to jokes or inappropriate sites can get you into trouble. You never know who may read it; if it is accidently distributed it's your name at the top.

Communication with any future employer should be carefully thought through. Be sure that you're talking to the decision maker and create a rapport with them. Listening during a job interview is just as important as presenting yourself.

Have a list of questions that show you understand the company and show your initiative. I avoid talking about my past in an interview and talk about where the company wants to go to demonstrate how my skill set will help them achieve that.

The reason you didn't get that deserved wage rise or promotion could be down to the way you communicated why you should. Think about what has already been said about appearance, non-verbal communication, and so on. Be honest with yourself. Did you perform as well as you could have in that moment?

Public Speaking

Communicating to a large audience is difficult at the best of times, but if you can master public speaking it will open up doors. The one thing holding us back from speaking in public is anxiety. Around 80% of people suffer from speech anxiety (glossophobia), making it the most common phobia.

Let's begin with ways to successfully manage the fear associated with public speaking.

Plan Well

Being mentally prepared and well organized, confident that you know what you're going to talk about, will calm the butterflies. We have spoken a lot about anxiety, and step one is feeling confident that you know what you're doing. It helps when you're talking about a topic that you're passionate about. If the passion isn't there, then it's wise to have a deep understanding of the subject matter, so you can handle any questions the audience might throw at you. We speak about 2.5 words per second, so a 10-minute speech requires around 1,500 words of material. Don't keep your script, swop it for key word notes written on cards, which will help you come across in a more natural way. What does any audience want? First off, they want to be entertained - they do want to learn something new, but mostly they want to be entertained. I'm not here to tell you how to write content, hold a microphone, or pause to create atmosphere, simply be entertaining. Practise then do a full dress rehearsal in front of a mirror. Take note of your gestures, body movements, and overall appearance. Use the 'borrowed genius' method. When you feel ready, record yourself with a phone or camera to help you evaluate your performance and make improvements before you go live. A practice run in front of a group can help you get used to talking to a crowd and getting a reaction.

What Is It That's So Frightening?

You're standing on a stage facing a few people (who are actually on your side) who want to be entertained for ten minutes. Then ...

... your neocortex logic presents you with a million scenarios of things going wrong; your limbic brain reminds you what happened the last time you did this; and your reptilian brain is saying, 'Standing here in the open, as the centre of attention, in front of a mob of strangers, with no weapon to protect you, spells immediate danger.' Then you receive a shot of adrenalin so you can decide whether to 'fight or flight'.

Regardless of who you are, from Bill Gates to Bill Clinton, this is what happens. Good speakers simply manage the process better than most.

Our physical response to both 'nervousness' and 'excitement' is similar. What you are feeling is because you care. You care about getting it right and doing a good job.

What if you saw the nervous energy as excitement? In NLP terms, you simply reframe, you make a decision to view this feeling as helpful and positive.

Let's pause here and look at a little motivation to help you practise public speaking. Bill Clinton earns just short of $2.7 million per year by giving speeches. Bill and Hilary together earned $6.725 million in speaking fees during 2015. Lance Armstrong starts at around $100,000 per talk. At the lower end of the scale it's not unrealistic to charge between $1,000 and $2,500 as a beginner who knows their onions. And, for those of you who cite a disability as the reason for not speaking in public, consider this. Kristie Lu Stout hosts a daily news programme for CNN and has a serious adenoid problem; Stephen Hawking didn't let his disability get in his way. Need I say more?

Where were we? Dealing with the excitement of walking on to that stage in front of a few people who want you to do well. Whatever you do, you want to arrive at the microphone psyched up and raring to go.

On the day, you should do your fitness routine. Arrive at the venue in good time so you can stand at the podium and get a feel of the stage. If you can rehearse beforehand, so much the better. What is going to calm your nerves with 30 minutes to go? I have many friends who are on stage 3-5 times a week. Some have a regular ritual, such as going for a walk, reiterating their main points, or being completely distracted by listening to heavy metal music right up until they walk on. If at this point you still have to practise, then you're in trouble. Create your own ritual to make you feel ready. It does not have to be meditation, although breathing deeply will help calm you. If you're an A-type personality you may find talking to people more helpful than locking yourself in the dressing room. If you're a B-type personality, then taking a walk or listening to some quieter music may help.

Don't worry about making mistakes, believe me, the biggest critic of your speech will be you. Go and watch others making speeches; see how many mistakes they make, note how they deal with it, and the audience reaction. The general public are very forgiving and 30 minutes after your talk is over, they have forgotten any blunders. If it was a 'big one' that made them laugh, then be thankful as you will be one of the few that will be remembered. Learn from your mistakes, after all, the next speech you give is to a fresh audience. Take a deep breath before you begin and off you go.

Remember what was said about building up your confidence? It has to do with taking a step forward each day. Practice talking in front of people whenever possible. I would highly recommend lessons. Toastmasters International is supportive of anyone who wants to learn this art. Classes will teach you about stage presence and techniques such as only drinking water that is at room temperature. Most of all they give you the opportunity to practise in front of real people who will be more sympathetic than your average crowd.

Let's Sum Up

Communicating is the only way to build strong relationships.

When it's important then only communicate face to face.

The tone of voice used can change your message.

Non-verbal cues reveal how others received your message.

Use non-verbal cues to really get your point across.

Listening is a big part of the communication skill set.

Talking with loved ones should involve more listening.

Electronic communications should be extra friendly.

Understand what your digital footprint looks like.

The workplace requires a more formal format.

Only you are holding yourself back from speaking in public.

What You Can Achieve

Good communication skills set you apart from the crowd.

Make a greater impact on everyone you meet.

Overcoming the fear of public speaking will open doors.

People treat you as they do,
because you let them treat you this way

~ Paul McQueen

CHAPTER TWELVE

People Skills

Connect

The ability to interact easily with others, to build and maintain meaningful relationships, requires a good communication style and highly developed people skills, sometimes called soft skills. Getting on with others, creating a rapport, showing empathy and respect, resolving conflict, negotiating, building trust, and winning people over to achieve your goals all require interpersonal skills that can be learned. Well-honed people skills will help you become more influential, impact everyone you meet, and help avoid misinterpretation of your message.

At First Sight

We looked earlier at what happens during first encounters and the importance of appearance, body language, and so on.

In the blink of an eye, the person you have just met has decided whether or not they like you. After which, it's pretty hard for them to change their mind, to the point that they will look for personal traits to back up this initial judgement. Why?

Well, the brain is a lazy beast and, after forming that initial opinion with help from the limbic brain, it requires loads of cognitive neocortex processing to figure out whether or not that snap decision was accurate. So, the easy way forward is to look for traits that supports the initial decision. This process is called confirmation bias.

As trustworthiness and attractiveness are the characteristics that are judged the quickest, confirmation bias is looking to confirm these two traits first. The right attire achieves this.

The person you have just met has not walked away, which indicates that they don't find you repulsive or dishonest. You've made a great first impression. What happens next?

The following five minutes decide whether this interaction will develop into a meaningful relationship or not. In order to own those first five minutes, you have to take charge by understanding what is happening on a subconscious level.

The Mechanics of the First 5 Minutes

When someone meets you for the first time they weigh up what you are like and how you behave in an attempt to forecast whether the relationship is going to benefit them in the future or whether pursuing it is a waste of their time. They then consider what their response should be to maximize those benefits.

What Value Will I Get From Being Your Friend?

The most significant research (Sunnafrank/Ramirez) on the consequences of long-term relations from assessments made during initial encounters confirmed that what happened during the first five minutes had a significant long-term influence.

This was a study of 258 students randomly paired with members of the same sex (to eliminate the sexual attraction factor) who were asked to get acquainted with one another. They were questioned after their first encounter as to: whether they liked the person; whether they felt similar to or different from that person; if they felt there was a value in pursuing a relationship with that person, ‚predicted outcome value' (POV).

Nine weeks later 164 agreed to be questioned on: how much they had communicated with the other person; and how close they had sat in the classroom during that time.

> ➢ Most participants knew from the first encounter if they liked each other or not. This means that first impressions

played a significant role, even after the first nine weeks.

➤ Those who had a positive first impression had more communication, admitted liking each other, sat closer together and felt it had influenced whether they considered themselves to be friends.

➤ Predicted outcome value (POV) was seen as the strongest predictor of future closeness in the relationship.

Much of what influences us during the first encounter and the first five minutes happens on a subconscious level. The main trigger to our decisions at this time is rapport.

Building a Rapport

Sometimes a rapport happens naturally if people have things in common or share a common interest, they simply hit it off. Mutual understanding and trust form the basis of a rapport in any interaction. This does not automatically mean that the parties have to like one another. Consider your relationship with your dentist, it is likely that you have a rapport with them - that being the case it was up to them to take the lead and establish that rapport with you.

Why limit your circle of friends to those who explicitly have an obvious commonality with you? There are times when it will be up to you to build a rapport with another person in situations where a common interest is not obviously present.

Having a rapport with someone will immediately take your interaction to another level. At which point you may find a multitude of shared interests. Showing a genuine interest in them and having the ability to listen are key. Rapport is created through 10% words and 90% non-verbal cues.

The premise for a rapport is:

people have a rapport with people who are like them or with people that they want to be like.

What You Can Say to Help Build a Rapport

Get the ball rolling with small talk on safe topics like shared experiences or the weather. Try not to talk about yourself and avoid direct questions, keep it general.

Listen and note any shared experiences that could expand the conversation. Let them do most of the talking. Find a topic they are deeply passionate about and let them tell you all about it.

Match their terminology. If they say 'I see that' then don't reply with 'I hear what you're saying', say 'I see that too'.

Insert some humour into the conversation, as laughter will make them relax and give you an early shared experience.

Show empathy by demonstrating that you can see their point of view - and don't forget to call them by their name.

Non-Verbal Cues That Help Build Rapport

People in agreement with one another will mimic each other's non-verbal cues. This is known as the chameleon effect. Next time you're out watch two friends in conversation, see how their body language and movements mimic one another. I have been in meetings where those in agreement all had the same posture.

Mirror the posture and movements of the other person (in a subtle way) to help create rapport.

Relax and lean slightly toward them to show that you are listening with interest, do not cross your arms or legs.

Maintain eye contact about 60% of the time. Smile - everyone reacts to a smile.

 hotlifestyle.info/int/rap

THE CRUX OF IT

Building a rapport begins with being welcoming, displaying appropriate relaxed body language, being open, showing empathy. Agreeing with and praising also builds a rapport. The most important factor is to use non-verbal cues.

By mirroring the other person you are subconsciously being agreeable in a way they can relate to.

What Makes People Like You?

Rapport is not something that you experience at the beginning of a relationship and can then forget about. It's an ongoing process, even after someone has decided that they do like you.

Showing a genuine interest in someone and the issues they are passionate about, being a good listener, letting them tell you about themselves, and taking them seriously all form the basis of them liking you. Spending time together and becoming familiar with each other will deepen a relationship. The more someone invests in a relationship the stronger it becomes and the more they like you.

People like people who are ‚warm' (non-competitive, friendly, and trusting) and are ‚competent' (who appear to have a high economic or educational status). One of the most important aspects in my opinion, if the relationship is to become intimate, is that you should both genuinely share the same values and belief systems.

The Benjamin Franklin Effect - Can I Ask You A Favour?

Franklin had an anecdote about when he was seeking reappointment as clerk to Philadelphia's General Assembly. A new member of the assembly was campaigning for another candidate but was not successful. Franklin wanted this new member's support and discovered that he possessed a collection of rare books. Franklin asked to borrow one of these books to which the new member agreed. A short time later Franklin returned the book with a note simply acknowledging the favour. The next time they met this new member started a conversation with Franklin offering his support. Franklin later wrote: 'He that has once done you a kindness will be more ready to do you another, than he whom you yourself have obliged.' This concept is called the Benjamin Franklin Effect.

Ask someone to do you a small favour. Don't be tempted to reciprocate in any way except to acknowledge it. The favour should cost them nothing in a monetary sense. When someone does you a favour they will tend to like you more as a result. They rationalize their actions by putting it down to the fact it was because they liked you. Let people invest in their relationship with you.

Leave people feeling better
for having met you

~ Paul McQueen

The Art of Persuasion

Do you know the phrase 'You can take a horse to water, but you can't make it drink'? Well, people are the same, they will only do what they want to do. Think carefully about this last sentence, it's the fine line between motivation and manipulation in the art of persuasion.

There are many times in our lives when we have to persuade someone. The first thing people think of is a sales situation, but there are many others. You have to persuade a company to employ you, or to give you that well-deserved raise, you want to ask the person of your dreams to go out on a date; or to convince your neighbour to be more considerate and keep the noise down. You should make being persuasive a habit.

You may have a rapport, they might even like you, but if you start with 'I have a problem', then they will think, 'and what's that got to do with me?' Phrase your problem in terms that are either neutral or that show how it affects them. For example, 'The problem is ...' or 'We have a problem with your ...'.

Coming to an agreement can often be as simple as stating the problem and asking them for a solution. Start the sentence with a positive spin. For example, 'I really like that sort of music but not at two o'clock in the morning, would it be too much trouble to turn it down?'

It is often best to negotiate a shared solution, such as, 'We have to share an apple, you can cut it, and I decide which half to take'. In other words, let them make the rules and you abide by them. People will be more persuaded if you can connect them emotionally to, and involve them in, the solution. Persuasion on the basis of 'a fair solution' cannot be argued with. Persuasion is only ever a win-win outcome. If you trick someone into something, or bombard them with your ideas, then this shows a 'lack' in the art of persuasion.

THE CRUX OF IT

1. Build a rapport.

2. Say what you have to say by starting with a positive.

3. Talk in terms of how it affects them or be neutral.

4. Listen to their viewpoint, agree with it, and thank them for it.

5. Find common ground with your idea.

6. Appeal through reason, evidence, or with a fair solution.

7. Connect them emotionally to the solution.

8. Be emotional about your pitch.

Dealing With Conflict

The best piece of advice I was given with regard to this was

be hard on the problem but soft on the person.

I have used this philosophy to great effect in many situations, especially when dealing with conflict. When you attack someone personally during a discussion they become defensive and take the position of an opponent. If, on the other hand, you focus on the issue while remaining non-confrontational, this involves them in the decision-making process to form a solution They work with you and not against you.

One of the first lessons I learned in sales was 'Win an argument, lose a sale'. Regardless of who you are dealing with, winning the argument will not have persuaded the other person to think differently. Arguments achieve nothing and leave a bad after taste with one of the parties. So, if your aim is to belittle someone then by all means start an argument with them. People who have a defensive disposition tend to argue a lot. If you genuinely want to find a solution to a conflict, then only by working with them will you form a long-term, mutually beneficial solution. Those with a high emotional intelligence (EQ) tend not to argue. Brush up your EQ.

 hotlifestyle.info/life/EQ

Manipulation Tricks

The Principle of Reciprocity

Have you ever sent someone a Christmas card because they sent you one first? Have you ever given money to someone because they pinned a badge on you? Your actions are being influenced by the principle of reciprocity, which is, if someone does you a favour, then you feel obliged to return that favour at some future date. Unscrupulous marketing people use this all the time to guilt you into buying something. When you recognize this trick simply say no.

A Sense of Loss

Be aware of the power this has, it goes deep in our psyche. Online gambling sites give you the first £10 for free. When you lose this money, you feel a sense of loss and want to gamble further to get ‚your' money back. The trigger is also prominent when a close relationship ends (you are dumped) or a loved one departs.

Scarcity

Sales people will often demonstrate a product then tell you only two are left. Even if you had no intention of buying anything up to that point your brain is provoked by the fact that there are only two left. Understand this trick and stay rational.

How to Say No and Be Assertive

Why do we wrestle with ourselves when we have to say ‚No' to someone? Often, we perceive a request as a command and our natural desire to avoid conflict has us saying yes when we really want to say no. Fear, anxiety, and guilt all play a role in becoming a ‚yes' person. You might think it's easier to say ‚yes' but you're not doing yourself or your company any favours by agreeing to every request. It is the fast way to burn out - especially if you feel you are being taken advantage of. You should learn to say NO!

You have every right to say no without feeling guilty. Do it politely so as not to offend. Practice saying no every day. Trust me, it's good for you.

Don't Costanza It

A Costanza is when you can't think of a quick retort and a great comeback line comes to you later. You then try to recreate the conditions for using your great line. Don't make them wait for your answer.

Trust Your Gut

Intuition is a good indicator. If it doesn't 'feel' right, don't do it. What's the cost of giving in? Time? Money? Health?

Don't Take Freebies

You have already read about the principle of reciprocity earlier. Taking the sample sausage offered by that nice lady at the supermarket makes it more likely that you'll buy them than if you hadn't accepted the freebie. Say 'No thanks!'

Because ...

Research has shown that using the word 'because' makes people agree with you (even when the reason you give is absolute rubbish). So instead of just saying, 'I'm sorry, I won't be able to help you move', try adding a reason (however trivial) to help your refusal go down more easily. Don't justify your 'no' too much, as it can seem like you're lying.

Use the Word 'Not'

'Not at this time', 'I'm not sure because', 'not now, maybe next time', 'not today thanks', 'I'd rather not thanks', 'that's not my thing'. This comes across as more agreeable than a definite no.

Air Your Discomfort

Someone asks to borrow money, be honest: 'I'm not comfortable lending money to anybody, sorry.'

Don't Be a Lemming

Just because others say yes doesn't mean you have to. Fight peer pressure.

I Wish I Could/It's an Honour You Asked

Normally I advocate the truth, but in some cases a little white lie never hurt anyone - along the lines of 'I wish I could help, but I'm tied up all week'.

You Can't Please All of the People All of the Time

Stop trying to please everybody. Worrying what people may think of you for saying no, is a waste of your time.

Say 'No' Twice When Necessary

Some people are persistent because they think you will simply cave in to their request if they ask enough times. Look them straight in the eye and say 'no thanks' a second time, more firmly than the first. It's more assertive if you say, 'I said no!'

What Are the Priorities Then?

You're handed yet another project, your plate is already full, and you have an employer who is only happy when you're bleeding. Be honest, ask what work takes priority, and tell them what will suffer as a result of the extra load.

 hotlifestyle.info/int/NO

The Power of Peer Pressure

Peer pressure is the influence of a social group or authority figure on an individual. Saying 'no' to our peers is the hardest thing to do. It is well documented in cases where, although their conscience objected to a request, someone still went along with it. We are conditioned from an early age to say yes to authority figures.

When complying with a request from our peers we feel that they are responsible for the actions that carry out the task. This was highlighted during the Nuremberg trials where the defence of 'I was just following orders' was used in the belief that their superior was the one responsible for the crimes committed. But they were all convicted.

Peer pressure from social groups affects us at an early age, whether it is to try that first cigarette or to dress the same. It's very hard to be different.

To fight peer pressure, you have to be strong and true to your own values. If you believe something is wrong, then resist the taunts. When your life is not being threatened, simply make a joke of the person(s) forcing you into their way of thinking.

 hotlifestyle.info/int/PP

Let's Sum Up

The first five minutes determine a relationship's prospects.

Predicted outcome value (POV) is a major deciding factor.

Building a rapport quickly creates a powerful connection.

Non-verbal cues quickly help you build a rapport.

People will like you for a variety of reasons.

Ask a favour and someone will like you more.

A persuasive habit leads to win-win situations.

Conflict? Be hard on the problem but soft on the person.

Start with something positive before stating a problem.

Be aware of manipulative tricks people use on you.

Say 'No' more often and don't let people abuse you.

When confronted with peer pressure be true to your values.

What You Can Achieve

Understanding soft skills helps you connect more easily.

Through creating a rapport you easily make more friends.

You can be less vulnerable to abuse by saying no!

*Body language influences how
people judge you but, more importantly,
it reveals how you see yourself*

~ Paul McQueen

CHAPTER THIRTEEN

Body Language

Make It Your First Language

Understanding the effect of your physical expressions on others is not half as important as understanding how they affect your own psyche.

How you carry yourself, sit, and walk says a lot about your personality and is an insight to your emotional state. A poor self-image can lead to low self-esteem, which is then portrayed by your posture, which people spot a mile off. Anxiety shows in subconscious self-pacifying behaviour - such as rubbing your neck, earlobe, or thigh, or with self-hugging - for all to see. It is important to control your own body language and learn to read that of others.

Strike the Pose

The 'fake it 'till you make it' experiment by Harvard University professor Amy J.C. Cuddy, showed that practising 'high-power' poses, even for short periods, promotes a sense of wellbeing and boosts confidence.

One group practised expansive high-power poses for one minute each: first pose, feet on the desk, hands behind head (The Obama); then, standing and leaning on one's hands over the desk (The Loomer). A second group did 'low-power', restrictive poses: sitting in a chair, arms folded; then standing with arms and legs crossed tightly. Saliva samples were used to measure testosterone and cortisol levels before and after posing. They were also asked to state how 'powerful' and 'in charge' they felt, on a scale from one to four.

In the high-power group, cortisol (a stress hormone that causes hypertension) levels dropped by about 25% and testosterone (a hormone linked to power and dominance) levels increased by about 19%, in both men and women. They also reported increased feelings of being powerful and in charge. In the ,low-power' group cortisol increased by about 17% and testosterone decreased around 10%. This is using body language to change your mindset, to boost your confidence, which changes outcomes.

Locking yourself in the bathroom before a job interview to practise a power pose for two minutes might just boost your confidence. Although some doubt that this achieves anything, for many people it does work. My thoughts are, try it. If it works for you then great, if not, there are other confidence-building techniques to try.

 hotlifestyle.info/int/pose

Standing Tall

Using attractive body language helps to communicate effectively with others for greater impact. Practise open body language. Take up as much space as possible with your palms facing upwards. Walk tall, without slouching or looking down at the floor or at your phone, demonstrating that you are in control. Imagine a string running through your spine and out through the top of your head, pulling you upwards, helping you stand taller. Walk with confidence and purpose, hands out of your pockets and down at your side.

When you're sitting, avoid low-power poses, such as crossing your arms or legs. Do regular exercises to strengthen your back and abdomen.

Use power poses in moderation when dealing with others. Too much and you can come across as arrogant. There's a happy medium between being confident and being modest.

Avoid Introvert Poses

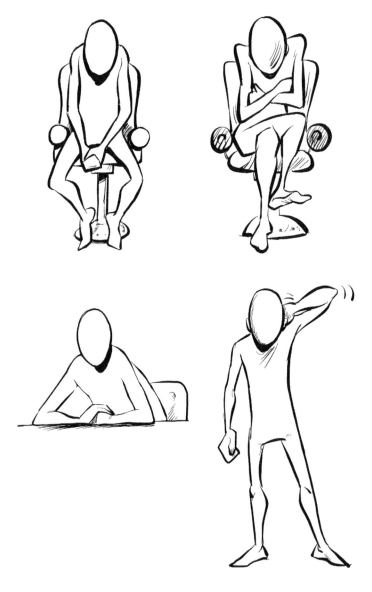

1. Hands folded in lap 2. Arms crossed 3. Arms crossed on table 4. Stroking neck

Practise Expansive Poses

1. The Obama 2. The Boss 3. The Loomer 4. Wonder Woman 5. The CEO

The Mechanics of Facial Expression

Facial expressions are vitally important for communication. They subconsciously display our true emotions to reveal our feelings of the moment.

A multitude of expressions emanate from the brainstem via a single nerve (the facial nerve), which branches out to all the facial muscles. The facial nerve is also wired to the neocortex. While spontaneous, 'real' emotions come from the brainstem, controlled expressions come from the neocortex, which is why deliberate facial expressions do not look the same as spontaneous ones.

Compare the result of a forced emotion (think of the phrase ,crocodile tears') with a spontaneous one (such as a smile). Some people can tell the difference between voluntary and involuntary facial expressions immediately.

The facial nerve plugs in to the same region of the brain that is responsible for processing fear, sadness, anxiety, rage, guilt, disgust, happiness, and sexual arousal. This fairly small region, called the amygdala, is found at the base of the brain on both right and left. It also controls emissions of the stress hormone cortisol.

The amygdala is considered to be part of the limbic system, which is why you smile when you remember a happy or funny situation.

Can Faking a Smile Make You Feel Happier?

The facial nerve connection is bi-directional. It routes signals from the brain to the muscles and directs feedback on the state of the muscle to the brain.

There has been some research into the idea that if you deliberately smile, your face muscles send feedback to your brain, which then influences your feelings and behaviour.

In a study on this facial feedback hypothesis, by Fritz Strack in 1988, half the participants were asked to hold a pen between their teeth with their lips open, to mimic a smile, the other half held the pen in their lips, to prevent them from smiling. They were then shown a cartoon and asked to rate it for humour. Those holding the pen between their teeth (smiling) rated the cartoon as more humorous. Although later research, with 1,894 participants, could not replicate Strack's findings.

A 2009 study at the University of Cardiff in Wales found that people who lost the ability to frown due to Botox injections were happier on average than people who could frown.

My suggestion is, try smiling more, if it works for you then use it as and when you need it. Don't smile too much in work/ meetings, which is actually a subservient behaviour.

Understanding Facial Expressions

We all agree that facial expressions and emotions are closely intertwined, and the ability to 'read' them is an important part of non-verbal communication. The real value in reading facial expressions is understanding how the other person is feeling so that you can guide your interaction accordingly.

There are seven universal expressions: surprise, disgust, fear, anger, sadness, contempt, and happiness. Get to know these expressions and the emotion behind them.

What Eyes Reveal

➢ When someone's gaze is on the top of your face they are feeling dominant. If their gaze is lower, between the eyes and the chin, this means they are paying attention.

➢ If someone's pupils get larger (dilate) while you are talking this can show they like you.

Eyebrows Can Be ...

➢ Raised and arched (in surprise)
➢ Lowered and knit together (showing anger)
➢ Inner corners drawn up (in sadness)

Mouth

➤ Biting lips (anxiety)

➤ Pursed lips (distaste)

➤ Covering mouth with hand (hiding something)

Hand Gestures

Judith Holler and Geoffrey Beattie from the University of Manchester, UK, found that using the right gestures can increase the value of your message by 60%, meaning people listen that much more. Hand gestures tend to be more spontaneous than posture and less prone to neocortex influence. In other words, they are a great indicator of a person's thoughts, which is why they are so powerful. They operate at a speed that we can easily follow, unlike facial expressions which tend to happen in the blink of an eye.

Show openness, sincerity, and honesty by holding your hands with open palms up, at a 45° angle (not directly up to the ceiling). If you hold your palms facing downwards you are expressing more authoritative and commanding behaviour. Think of the loomer pose, palms down on the table. Extending hand gestures within someone's personal space, can engage them more in the conversation. Do this with an open hand.

Similarly, with the universal gesture of greeting by shaking hands, if you offer your hand palm down (authoritative), forcing the other person to grasp with their palm upwards, you are showing dominance. Think of the phrase 'getting the upper hand'.

If you are trying to achieve a rapport with someone who is obviously nervous, consider offering a submissive handshake with your palm turned slightly upwards.

The use of a two-handed shake, where your second hand is placed on top, can make a stranger feel uncomfortable. A good starting point is to offer your hand vertically showing that you are on an equal footing. If the person then tries to get the upper hand, don't fight it, but do make a note that they are trying to dominate you. It's important to make direct eye contact while shaking hands, this reinforces any rapport.

Gauge the firmness of your handshake to match that of the other person. If you're not sure, then squeeze until you feel pressure on your skin, and then stop.

Do you suffer from sweaty palms? The other person will read this as a sign of anxiety. Wipe them with a handkerchief or try holding a cold beverage with a serviette, swopping hands just before shaking. Pumping hands one to three times is usual, don't overdo it.

 hotlifestyle.info/int/HS

> **THE CRUX OF IT**
>
> There are hundreds of hand gestures you can use to help you get your message across, with lots of examples on the Internet.

The Language of Success

Don't over smile. Sure, when building up a rapport it is important, but during meetings and job interviews curb it a little. You may have noticed that leaders smile less, while their subordinates smile at them. Two things are at play:

1. The friendlier you are, the less you are perceived as competent.

2. Smiling is a subservient gesture that nervous people do a lot.

Fidgeting shows nervousness and a lack of confidence. Take control of your non-verbal cues. Use mindfulness to step back and view yourself. Many people don't even notice when they're drumming on the table with their fingers or constantly touching their hair or face. Practice being still when someone is talking, it's the sign of a leader.

Handshakes on first encounters, when you are trying to establish a rapport, should be matched. Handshakes with work colleges or subordinates should be firm and offer your hand vertically. A firm handshake shows character and confidence, especially if you're closing a deal, make it sit. Make eye contact and pump no more than three times.

Stand tall, in a relaxed manner, with your feet slightly apart. Posture says lots about your emotional state.

The Seven-Day Interactions Challenge

Notice how you walk and sit for a week. Try to walk taller, with your chin up, and with purpose. Deliberately use open body language, which could be as simple as spreading your feet a little further apart than usual when talking to others. No crossed arms or legs and avoid those introvert poses.

Practice using more hand gestures for a week, especially showing your palms, and note the results. This does not mean waving your arms around like a crazy person. Keep it subtle.

Purposely use The CEO pose once this week in public.

Let's Sum Up

Non-verbal cues account for 60% of your message.

Practice 'encoding' by optimizing the signals you send out.

Practice 'decoding' the non-verbal cues of others.

Practice power poses to boost your confidence.

Use open body language, take up space and stand tall.

Be aware that low-power poses make you look anxious.

Facial expressions divulge every emotion you're feeling.

Properly used hand gestures make a positive impact.

Certain non-verbal cues will make a big impact every time.

What You Can Achieve

You will make a bigger impact and influence other people.

They will take you more seriously and listen more.

You will be more attractive to others.

You will be perceived as more confident and competent.

You will feel more relaxed when meeting others.

Intimacy requires respect first

~ Paul McQueen

CHAPTER FOURTEEN

Intimacy

A Communion of Souls

When where you last intimate with someone? What? You had sex only last week I hear you say. Let me start again.

Do you yearn for closeness? The majority of us certainly do, but not everybody it seems. Some people fear that opening up makes them vulnerable to a devastating pain when the relationship ends. So, what is it exactly?

Intimacy is left open to interpretation, it happens when trust and respect are present, and you feel truly connected to someone. We are most passionate when we want total acceptance from another person.

More Than Just the Physical

Today, the word intimacy has taken on a sexual connotation, but it's not a purely physical thing. For true fulfilment in your relationship you need much more than just sex.

Each of us has five significant needs in our lives. Not only the physical, but also the emotional, the intellectual, the social, and the spiritual. All of which are designed to work together in harmony. In our search for intimacy we want it today, we want instant gratification. When the need for intimacy in a relationship is not met, we look for an 'instant' solution. Where do we look? To the physical. It's easier to be physically intimate with someone than to be intimate in any of the other four areas. You can become physically intimate with another person in an hour, or even half an hour - it depends on the urge! But you soon discover that sex may only be a temporary relief for a superficial desire and you are left with a deeper need that is still unmet.

Intimacy really means 'total life sharing'. Haven't we all had the desire at one time or another for closeness, for oneness, for sharing our life with someone, totally?

Many people won't be interested in intimate sex with you on the first date, and possibly not on the second. Why is that? Because they need to get to know you well enough, they want a non-sexual intimacy with you first.

Non-Sexual Intimacy

Some people wonder how on earth is it possible to be intimate with someone without envoling sex? I'm neither condoning nor promoting abstinence; the point here is to explain the other facets of intimacy.

If non-sexual intimacy plays no role in your relationship and it is based only on sex, it will not be fulfilling and will lead to frustration. An expression of closeness is a human need that has nothing to do with sex. Developing and growing different types of intimacy will deepen the love in your relationship, and their presence will make your sex more intense.

Emotional Intimacy

Building a deep emotional connection with your partner means you can share joy, pain, and tears. Where can you learn about developing emotional intimacy? I don't think you can learn it. It's being completely honest about your feelings, being vulnerable, sharing your innermost thoughts, and truly listening when they speak. Understanding and taking care of your partner's emotional needs and being aware of their feelings (showing empathy) creates an emotional bond. The depth of emotional connection is probably the strongest indicator of being in love with someone. Laughing together, crying together, and building emotional ties means expressing your deepest feelings without fear of being judged.

Intellectual Intimacy

Trading thoughts about things you passionately care about. An exchange of ideas and opinions after watching a good film for example. A meeting of minds connecting on the plane of ideas builds intellectual intimacy.

Social Intimacy

Social intimacy has to do with doing things together in public. This could be going to the cinema or playing mini golf. Whether it is just the two of you or a group, this sort of public display enhances our sense of intimacy. You could view it as team building.

Spiritual Intimacy

Sharing awe-inspiring moments, like a walk in the mountains or watching a sunset from a sandy beach. Being spiritually attuned to one another without needing to say anything. You share common ethics, qualities, and morals. You know that your fates are entwined for both the short and the long term.

THE BOTTOM LINE

Talking to your partner about intimacy can actually help it flourish. Are you feeling disconnected in any one of the four areas mentioned? Shared experiences (good and bad) bring people together more closely than sex on its own.

Fear of Intimacy

Marshall Hodge wrote Your Fear of Love in which he says, 'We all long for moments of expressions of love, closeness and tenderness, but frequently, at the critical point, we often draw back. We are afraid of closeness. We are afraid of love.' Later in the same book Hodge says, 'The closer you come to somebody, the greater potential there is for pain.' It is the fear of pain that often drives us away from finding true intimacy.

'Tis better to have loved and lost,
than never to have loved at all

~ Alfred, Lord Tennyson

Opening yourself up to someone, sharing your innermost thoughts, making yourself vulnerable to potential pain, can seem very scary to some. Finding someone you can build a relationship with based on mutual love and trust is not so easy. We have all been hurt at some time, the younger we are the more it hurts. I believe you should tread carefully at the beginning of any relationship, take it to the next level one step at a time, learn each other's ways of interacting then push the envelope. If you simply stop trying, you'll miss out on one of the most wonderful experiences you can have with another person; that of being completely accepted, without conditions, being yourself.

Finding the Perfect Partner

There's a tendency to go along with a relationship until the next best thing comes along. Jumping from one partner to another, waiting for the person that will sweep you off your feet to ride into the sunset, happy ever after.

This means not committing to, nor investing 100% in, a relationship because it doesn't match the mind picture for how it should be. I'm not suggesting that you stay with someone who makes you miserable, but if you are not committed then the other party feels it and behaves accordingly. They are not committed either, and both of you wonder why the relationship eventually fails.

Every relationship that you care about has to be worked on. If you're not ready to commit to physical intimacy, then invest your time and effort in building non-sexual intimacy to find out how compatible you are. It's my experience that relationships based only on sex are not fulfilling and are short lived. Don't make the goal having sex all the time. It is not a benchmark for judging how a relationship is progressing.

There are possibly only four people on the whole planet who are 100% compatible with you. Where will you meet them?

 hotlifestyle.info/PP

Love Rules

Do you share the same core values? What is non-negotiable for you? The desire to get married; having ten kids; your definition of honesty ...

Are you shown the respect you deserve? This is shown in small things: being late without calling; making plans with friends at weekends without including you; not pulling their weight with household chores ...

Are your emotional and sexual needs catered for? Do they show empathy at times when you are down? Are they lazy in bed, expecting you to always take the active role?

Are they caring enough? Is your concern for their wellbeing reciprocated or not?

These are some of the questions you should be asking during the first few weeks after meeting someone. Intimacy begins with respect and grows over time.

At the end of the day though, love rules.

Let's Sum Up

There are five facets of intimacy for a fulfilling relationship.

Don't let fear get in the way of growing deeper feelings.

Love the one you're with and show commitment.

Libido = Appetite²

~ Paul McQueen

CHAPTER FIFTEEN

Sexuality

More Sex Please, We're British

If you're offended by words like penis and vagina, then before you take this book outside to burn it, consider using this chapter for some exposure therapy.

Most of us haven't chosen our sex, it was there at birth, produced by whatever collection of hormones gathered at conception. People who get to choose their sex should see it as a blessing, although this single decision is probably one of the hardest that any human must make within their lifetime. Making the right decision will make you much happier. Are you happy with your sex?

Sexuality, on the other hand can be more fluid and - depending on our experiences, likes, and dislikes - we will choose to go with the triggers that turn us on.

We can change our sexual preference at any stage in our lives. By which I mean, you may have preferred skinny people and then be turned on by a fuller figure.

We have different sexual needs (libido) at different times in our lives. Libido is a measure of the urge/appetite to engage in sexual activity. It can be affected by hormone levels, stress, psychological, social, and physical problems, medications (such as aphrodisiacs), or age. An enormous variability exists in human sexual behaviour - asexuality, celibacy, sadism, masochism, hetero, lesbian, gay, transgender, bisexual, fetishist, objectophilia (love of inanimate objects), zoophilia - the options are so broad that if you chose a different one each week you would never get bored. Funny thing is, we don't. We tend to have one narrow option that rocks our sexuality boat and we stick with it. Some people are so set in the belief that their sexual orientation is the right one they become enraged toward those who don't practice the same orientation. It's natural to explore your sexual desires as long as all participants are over the age of consent and are willing.

I won't simply highlight biological differences between the sexes (men vs women) as this will achieve very little. The aim of this book is to facilitate a better understanding to promote a Hotlifestyle for all.

Female Sexuality - What Men Should Know

Now that it's just us lads huddled around the camp fire, let's talk about sex. The female sex drive is an infinitely complex subject. There have been volumes written about it and numerous studies offer, at best, sketchy insights and contradictory conclusions. When surveys show that some 30% of women admit to having no desire, we should take a closer look at understanding how women experience arousal and desire and at their motivation.

The notion that 'only men have sex, women just join in' is sometimes understandable when you consider the passive role many women take in the bedroom. But consider this.

Societal pressure to regulate female desire has contributed to curbing lust. Our culture punishes women who openly express promiscuity by suggesting there is something wrong with a woman who loves sex, which creates repression and inhibition. Studies suggest that women tend to have a negative attitude toward their bodies ... but, let's face it lads, not only do women go to work, we award them the privilege of looking after every aspect of the home (cooking the dinner, washing socks and undies, doing the shopping) and then we wonder why they don't behave like a nymphomaniac in the bedroom, tending to our every sexual need. It's a funny world, isn't it lads?

In addition, some birth-control pills can result in reduced levels of those hormones that boost the libido, contributing further to a lack of sex drive.

So, we have stigma, repression, inhibition, hormones, inconsiderate partners, tiredness, shame, and even sin all contributing to a waning sex drive. Add to that stress, work, and family, you'd think there should be a pill to deal with it all?

Pills to improve the male sex drive target genital capillaries. Blue pills are often taken because there is a problem in the relationship or partners are no longer attractive. The resulting lack of lust is expressed through the lack of an erection. The pills create the erection but not the desire. Pharmaceutical companies admit that the main difficulty in creating a drug for female desire is that women appear to be driven by the mind, not the body. Could it be that both sexes might simply have the same problem?

To round it off, let's consider the 60% of women who admit to lust, I can safely say that few engage in sex for the sake of it. Far from being a ‚let's just f...' kind of sexuality, it's more of a reactive process to getting emotionally aroused first.

Research suggests that the amount of intimacy experienced is a deciding factor for sexual encounters. In other words, no sex without some form of non-sexual intimacy. But even that is no guarantee that there is an interest in sex.

Don't assume that she has explored her own body and sexuality in the same way that you probably have. Women generally have a different relationship to their vaginas than you do to your penis. They don't talk to it for one thing!

What Does A Woman Want?

Sigmund Freud (neurologist and founder of psychoanalysis, 1856-1939) posed this very question a century ago and we still don't have a satisfactory answer.

Sexologists in the 1960s began to look for the reasons why most women don't have the same sex drive as men. With the birth-control pill taking away some of the consequences of sex and the women's liberation movement the lust factor has still never matched that of men.

Why are studies so problematic? Have you ever tried to ask on a first date, 'Do you like to orgasm?' This subject might be pondered over in the safety of a national magazine but when confronted by a man (remember the two assessments on a first encounter intention/capability) who could act on it. The reaction might be a slap to the face.

Education in the arena of female orgasm has been lacking for many years but it is getting better. Women seem really cagey when it comes to talking about it but less so when it comes to faking it. A UK survey by Durex in 2017 found that 1 in 10 fake an orgasm at least once a week. Are you fellas to blame? The survey went on to say that 89% of men focus on their partner having a big O. So, what's going wrong?

Do women actually want to orgasm? Sometimes yes, but it does not seem to be the primary goal in all encounters.

The Mechanics of the Female Orgasm

Women who don't orgasm through intercourse alone have been wrongly termed as dysfunctional. This notion is placed in the minds of men by the porn industry, which shows women exploding in instant ecstasy upon penetration and climaxing together shortly after. A study released in February 2017 found that 1 in 5 women surveyed admitted that they never reached orgasm through intercourse alone. A further third said that they needed clitoral stimulation during intercourse in order to orgasm. Another third said that their orgasm felt better when clitoral stimulation was included during intercourse.

I am always surprised by how many men are ignorant of this fact and who believe that as long as they can keep going she will eventually reach a climax through intercourse (why do 1 in 10 fake it?). Some men feel their masculinity is undermined if they have to perform clitoral stimulation during the act, believing that penetration should simply be enough. Maybe it's time us fellas had a rethink how we go about it. Dare I say it? Practice makes perfect. Try a new routine or talk about it if she is willing.

THE CRUX OF IT

Most women don't orgasm through intercourse alone.

Ladies First

As said earlier, orgasm is not always the goal when sleeping together. For some women being desired or sharing moments of intimacy are the orgasm. If the goal is orgasm, then it's probably a good idea to practise 'ladies first'. The chances of you climaxing simultaneously, as in those porn films, is very slim. Women can experience multiple orgasms and might experience a second round as you work your magic. It is not the intention here to teach you techniques for clitoral stimulation, but you might like to look up terms like 'oral sex' or 'cunnilingus'.

So, the main sex organ in women is the clitoris and not the vagina, although sexologist Beverly Whipple tried to establish the existence of the G spot in the 1980s. It is still a matter for discussion in sexologist circles and it has not really been proven that it exists.

Many women require a lot of foreplay to get aroused. The female body looks pretty much the same whether aroused or not, so knowing when she would like penetration is often difficult. Due to the passive nature of many women, and bad communication, how can you really know if you have consent? Asking in a direct manner can ruin the atmosphere so be subtle and watch the signs. Arousal is not consent.

Motivating her to take the lead could be the answer.

What Are Her Motivations?

Defining what a woman wants poses a huge dilemma. On the one hand she wants to feel safe and protected, and on the other she wants to be pinned against a wall and be ravished. The fantasies women have don't always translate into what they actually want to happen. It is the pleasures of the mind versus the terrors of reality when you consider that 1 in 10 women indulge in rape fantasies. Women's erotic fantasies focus on getting pleasure, while men's tend to involve giving it.

It's not uncommon for women to use their charms to get what they want. Which is often a stable, financially secure, loving relationship for which they are willing to 'let you' perform. Women look for signs of prosperity or social status when choosing a mate, someone well dressed and well groomed. Money and power are incredible aphrodisiacs (although smell plays an important role, with bad breath rating as the biggest turn off).

Most women think in terms of long-term relationships, someone who can provide materially while rearing a family. Remember though, this is on a subconscious level that can be traced back to when life on earth was much tougher.

It's not through a lack of research that Freud's question goes unanswered, it may simply be unanswerable.

Male Sexuality - What Women Should Know

Time for some girl talk. Male sexuality is fairly straightforward, an open book really. Physical (visual) attraction drives male sexuality, regardless of emotional ties. Patterns and preferences are usually clearly defined triggers, focusing on some part of the female anatomy or clothing. Penetration and orgasm are the ultimate goal, whereby sex ends shortly after ejaculation. There is generally no shortage of desire, and should it wane, then by pressing the right button, whoops, there it is. As men don't fake their erections, they can be an excellent indicator as to how sexy they find you. Most men (89%) really do try to pleasure their partner, whether they have the right technique is another question, but you could always guide them. Don't assume that he knows what he's doing. Expressing your wishes could be beneficial, as most men are very accommodating.

This behaviour is embedded in male genes and is often a result of hormones. Research on 28 males aged 21-45 showed that an abstinence from ejaculation of just seven days saw a spike on serum testosterone levels. If you are looking for more sensuality in the bedroom as opposed to a heated rush, consider the frequency of your lovemaking. After two weeks of celibacy, serum testosterone levels will increase his desire to boiling point. Remember, your sex drive is probably lower than his, and don't think he's being rational at this point. One solution could be to make the first night an opportunity for him to 'release' his desire. Then with his testosterone levels at a manageable level you will be surprised, when you take the lead and slow the pace, how your man will copy your moves and willingly be guided.

What Does A Man Want?

The desire for regular sex is probably the main reason that most men get married. When a long-term relationship is sought, his ideal will be a youthful, fertile, healthy partner with no children. He will also weigh up her behaviour with regard to fidelity.

Men want to feel invited and feel appreciated for their efforts during the act. As men are very visual, dressing in a sexy outfit can be very important. Orientation differs greatly so asking for his preferences might be a good idea.

Let's Sum Up

Most of us didn't choose our sex.

Sexuality/sexual orientation is anything you want it to be.

Women generally have a lower sex drive than men.

Most women can't orgasm through intercourse alone.

Educate your partner and buy them a copy of this book.

The goal of male sexuality is penetration and orgasm.

Final Thoughts on Interactions

Creating a strong healthy relationship requires give and take. Listening is one of the most important skills for interacting successfully.

Remembering and using someone's name will set you off on good footing. Emphasizing your point with good use of body language, making others feel important and comfortable around you and you will have everyone you meet liking you, listening to you, and wanting to be in your company.

Developing strong people skills and understanding the importance of rapport and the impact you make in the first five minutes will help you to succeed.

Intimacy is much more than just the physical. Getting to know someone (of either sex) on different levels will deepen your relationship. Understanding the intimate needs of your partner and acting on them will help you grow together with that special person. Being the best friend of the one you love and being there in times of need is the best recipe for a long-term relationship. Make creating strong personal relationships your priority.

At the end of this book you should have an idea of how each theme is intertwined with the others. Practice the techniques learned here and you will be amazed by their impact on others.

BOOK FOUR

ENTERPRISE

Find Your Vocation,
Then Boldly Go Forward

Some regard private enterprise as if
it were a predatory tiger to be shot.
Others look upon it as a cow
that they can milk.
Only a handful see it for what it really is -
the strong horse that pulls the whole cart.

~ Sir Winston S. Churchill

INTRODUCTION

Whatever your current situation, it's the result of choices you have made - whether you're destitute, working in a dead-end job, or you're a successful entrepreneur. Only the successful admit this fact, while others want to blame everyone else for their predicament. Realizing that your situation is the result of your choices is important to leading a Hotlifestyle.

Are you living to work or working to live? These are two radically different lifestyle choices, neither of which is wrong. If work is just a means to earn money so you can pursue other activities, then a work-life balance will be important to you. If you bring your work home most evenings and continue to think about work at weekends then you may not be aware of the importance of a work-life balance.

How do you see your financial situation in five years? Do you think like Del Boy, 'This time next year we'll be millionaires', but don't have a plan to back it up? Or have you thought of a realistic way forward?

Enterprise is in our DNA. We got this far, because our ancestors traded across continents, took risks, reaped the rewards, and invested.

Let's look at this exciting subject.

If you're not bleeding,
then they're not happy

~ Paul McQueen

CHAPTER SIXTEEN

Career

Employed vs Self-Employed

I can look back on 40 years of a working life and safely say that being employed in a company, however large or small, was the closest I ever came to experiencing a battlefield. Employers' expectations have become more and more unreasonable. If you're not bleeding, then management are not happy.

I have always had a first-class work ethic and was of the opinion that my job was like a marriage, if I wasn't 100% behind the company then I simply quit. I lived to work most of my life and have been happiest when running my own projects and companies, and most miserable when employed.

Is becoming an entrepreneur all it's cracked up to be? Entrepreneurs work longer hours just to avoid being employed. All that responsibility, self-motivation, risk, and multitasking is certainly not for everybody. But I would recommend that those considering this route think carefully before taking the leap into self-employment.

Many countries have played about with and tested the idea of giving people a guaranteed income, a model that pays enough so you don't have to work unless you want to. Experiments in the Netherlands and Scotland showed that people who received a guaranteed income didn't just sit in front of the telly getting drunk. Some 90% took the initiative and turned their hobbies into money-making ventures or started a lifestyle business.

This is my view of being employed vs being self-employed.

Employment	Self-Employment
Get a job	Start a business
Make a company rich	Make money for yourself
Fixed income wage	Earn what you're worth
Pay big taxes	Offset taxes and pay less
Work 40 hours per week	Work whenever you want
Frustrated by the workplace	Freedom and satisfaction
Deal with line managers	Deal with clients
Promote company image	Be respected in the market

Ready to Give Up Your Day Job?

You hate your job? Don't be too hasty. Starting your venture toward financial freedom requires extensive planning. Try using positive affirmations to help you get on in your current position so that you are prepared and in control when it comes to quitting. Try saying to yourself on the way to work, 'Continuing here will take me to the next step'.

Do you have what it takes? Going it alone can be very rewarding in terms of satisfaction with a job well done and the financial aspect. To begin with, you will work long hours, putting your skills to the test, and being accountable, and you will need oodles of confidence. If you're not practised in dealing with clients, stress, or deadlines, consider dipping your toe in the water; build up your business in your spare time, backed up by the security of your job. How have you dealt with failure in the past? Are you a mover and shaker? You need to answer all these questions and be brutally honest with yourself. Be prepared to hire people with the skills that you don't have.

 hotlifestyle.info/fail

Do you have a plan? Do you have a clear understanding of what you will do? Do you have a client base to start you off? Most small businesses fail within the first year due to a lack of realistic planning and a shortfall in start capital. A business plan should include an estimated cash flow, so you can judge if you're winning. Setting goals, with an action plan for achieving them, are paramount to your success.

Do you have a network of friends and colleagues to bounce ideas off and help motivate you toward your goals? Yes, show them your goals, there is nothing more motivating than peer pressure.

Consider a lifestyle business. The main motivation here may not be riches but allowing you to use your talents while earning a living. The original version of this is running a corner shop but now technology has opened up a multitude of opportunities for lifestyle businesses, especially with the advent of affiliate marketing. You can earn from a book, a blog, a YouTube channel, online courses, an online shop ...

You can work from the comfort of your own home, which means you can work when you want to. I tended to work more hours than when I was in an office. This might not be for everyone as you don't have the office camaraderie.

 hotlifestyle.info/ent/LB

Are you really convinced that you have a fantastic idea? Have you received great feedback from your friends? Do your homework first to work out how you will bring it to market before you quit your job or invest too much time and money. Investigate how comparable ideas were marketed and choose a similar route. The biggest selling point about your company is you. Don't sell yourself short. You should be promoting 'you' all the time.

 hotlifestyle.info/ent/ENT

The Future of the Workplace

There is no doubt that the workplace is changing out of all recognition, which is creating new opportunities for some while leaving others behind. How can you adapt to stay relevant and to secure a future? More than half the kids attending primary school today will be engaged in a type of job that doesn't yet exist. The World Economic Forum expects a net increase in jobs by 2026, in every industry except production, which will be heavily automated.

Key to staying relevant in a more automated workplace is the ability to adapt and a willingness to undertake ongoing education. Work involving problem solving, critical thinking and creativity will always be needed. This change is being driven by the Internet of Things, big data, cloud technology, CPU processing power, energy supply, women's aspirations, an ageing population, climate change ...

 hotlifestyle.info/FW

Find Your Vocation

Changing tack halfway through your career can be a real challenge, which makes it all the more important to work out early on what you want to do. Choose a job that you're passionate about and you will never have to work, or so they say. My experience is that people who find their vocation tend to work above and beyond the call of duty and become experts. So, if you're just starting out and have limited work experience, how do you know what you will be good at in five years' time? Will your skill set be relevant in view of automation? Rather than asking 'What am I good at?', ask 'What could I become good at?' It will open up a lot more possibilities.

Initially, you should look at some broad preferences, such as office work, hand work, professional, sales, self-employed, save the planet, military, and so on. What environment do you see yourself working in? It is as important to know what you don't want to do.

How well do you deal with stress? Are you good at talking to people or are you more introvert? What will you be like in five years? The shy introvert student might not be so shy a year after reading this book. Confidence is only a question of stepping a little deeper into the water each day.

The key is to keep an open mind and experiment with different kinds of work. If you believe your forte is writing for example, then write some articles and submit them.

Experiment with Different Kinds of Work

You can talk about being a doctor, an accountant, or an estate agent, but the only way you will ever know if that kind of work suits you is to get out there and try it. You shouldn't go into a job blind, especially if you have to train for, say, seven years.

If you have a desire to work in a particular industry - media, medical, legal, construction, or car manufacture - then get work experience in that business at any level. If you're at university, use the summer break to investigate companies/institutions and work as an intern. Working as a temp can also open doors.

I understand the things that I really like to do only because I have had work experience in a variety of industries. Regardless of my job title (TV producer or publisher) it always felt like I was in sales and I always felt I was creating something. These are two criteria that I have set for a satisfying job. I changed careers about every four years, often moving to a different country as well.

It's obvious, with a job that you are passionate about you are more likely to become an expert, which people will notice. The rule is, if you spend 80,000 hours at something you like doing, then you will become very good at it. That's roughly how long it takes, whether you want to work in sales or become an accountant.

Ask people you trust what type of work they see you doing. They might come up with occupations you didn't think of. As mentioned in the section on Empowerment, others see you differently to the way you see yourself, and they are often more accurate when it comes to understanding your personal traits. Don't rely on one person, ask family, friends, work colleagues, or even your boss.

Use your commuting time wisely for brainstorming. Write the burning question at the top of a notepad, 'What kind of work would I enjoy?' Include the ideas from people you have spoken to and consider where you would like to be, regardless of your current situation. When you feel your list is complete put it in order of preference. Then think how you could try out the job in position one on your list. Remember, it's only by trying out different jobs that you will know which one suits you.

Talk to a job agency or head hunter, if you are not straight out of education and have had some work experience. Be aware though, they will push you in a direction where you already have experience. I remember when I was 40 and an agent told me in no uncertain terms that my career was over and there was no prospect of ever getting a job. Thank goodness I decided not to believe him and went on to some of my best paid work. Make it your job to find work that gets you up in the morning. If you don't have the skill set, then acquire it!

Keep investing in yourself!

You will spend roughly one-third of your life working so enjoy what you do. Are you following a well-thought-out career path or simply hoping for an opportunity? How committed are you to making your life an amazing journey?

Read our five-part series, Winning Mindset:

 hotlifestyle.info/ent/WM

Let's Sum Up

The points to consider about going self-employed are:

You will earn what you're worth when you work for yourself.

More responsibilities and risks are involved in going it alone.

Do it for the right reasons and plan carefully.

You might consider starting with a lifestyle business.

Make sure you stay relevant by upgrading your skill set.

What do you think you may be good at in the future?

Experiment with different kinds of suitable jobs.

What You Can Achieve

More job satisfaction and respect by working for yourself.

Everything you do, you will own, and you can build on it.

Financial freedom, with a lot of fun on the way there.

*Real wealth is knowledge
and a pocket full of fun*

~ Paul McQueen

CHAPTER SEVENTEEN

Wealth Creation

A Wealth of Experience

Would you describe yourself as wealthy? How would you know if you were wealthy? We started this book looking at financially wealthy people with solid careers who all committed suicide. A lot of good being wealthy was for them you might say. You could have a wealth of experience, or a wealth of knowledge, or even a wealth of good qualities, does this make you wealthy? In today's society it's safe to say that those who have accumulated a lot of things and have an obscene amount of money in the bank are considered wealthy. Whether they are living a fulfilling, amazing Hotlifestyle is the question.

If you can't appreciate the simple things in life, then money alone won't help you.

Most everybody likes money and wants lots of it. Nobody I've spoken to however has actually shown me a plan for creating wealth. With the average debt (excluding mortgages) in the UK at about £8,000 per person, and in the USA over $6,000, it seems that most people do need a plan to reduce debt first, as they are financially squeezed by taking on too much debt. Being debt free is always better than having a flash car, a big house and a major debt. Because ...

MONEY COSTS MON£Y

When you consider that the average credit card interest rate is 23% (APR) and lenders can obtain money at under 1%, they are on to a really good thing, whereas you are not.

The first step toward wealth creation is managing your personal finances to get your current situation in order. If you are in debt, make clearing it your priority.

Restructure

Begin by consolidating all your high interest credit into one lower interest bank loan (check APR), which you can extend over a longer period. This should make your monthly payments smaller, freeing up some cash each month and allowing you to pay off other accumulated debt. Regardless of your financial position carrying out this exercise simply makes sense.

Do an Audit to Understand Your Present Situation

1. **Write down your household's monthly income.**

2. **Write down your household's monthly expenditure -** including any regular loan payments.

3. **Subtract one from the other.** Is the number positive?

Don't be surprised if it is a negative number, so many people are living beyond their means. Start living within your means and see what can be done to make this number positive. How much can you afford to pay off loans each month?

Set Realistic Financial Goals

To create wealth, you need to eliminate debt. Draw up a realistic plan to reduce your loans to zero over a set period.

There are only three options to alleviate debt:

1. Earn more

2. Spend less

3. Default on the loan, which affects your credit rating

Don't put off setting goals in the belief things might get easier. Not acting now is simply procrastination and wishful thinking. Time to get real! Keep control of repayments, because if a creditor decides to pull the plug and foreclose on the loan it will be very expensive.

Cars - Buy, Finance, Lease or Share?

An accountant once told me: 'Buy things that appreciate in value and rent/lease items that depreciate over time.'

Tying up vast amounts of money in a new car that can depreciate by as much as 35% in the first year can be a hard cookie to swallow. Depreciation rates get lower on cars that are over three years old, meaning you will suffer less if you buy a 3-5-year-old car. To maintain its resale value keep evidence of regular servicing, keep the mileage low, and repair any damage.

It's also important to note that not all cars depreciate at the same rate. Paying cash for a quality second-hand car that is over three years old is the most economical way to own a car.

The thrill of driving a new car, with that distinct new car smell, three-year warranty, and reduced maintenance costs make owning one very tempting. You could consider financing - which means that you'll eventually own it - or leasing - whereby you never own the vehicle and return it at the end of the contract period, usually three years. Be aware that leases always have mileage limits, with hefty penalties if you go above that limit. Leasing is only beneficial when you can offset the costs against taxes, as with a company. If this is not possible then buying a new car, even with finance, will almost always be a better deal than leasing. Alternatively consider using a car sharing scheme if you are not reliant on your car every day.

Why Home Ownership Is So Important

Getting a foot on the property ladder is difficult in some regions more than others. The reasons for owning your home are obvious: you have got to live somewhere; what you pay in rent will often cover mortgage repayments and the property increases in value over time.

When the value of the property increases more than the mortgage interest rate then, technically, the mortgage is costing you nothing and it has become a saving scheme.

Let's face it, the hindrance to home ownership for most people is raising the initial deposit. Taking that first step is key to financial freedom. You may have to start small and grow your equity until you can trade up to a larger property.

First Steps to Becoming Financially Savvy

➢ Stop living beyond your means and know how much you can spend each month
➢ Prioritize expenditure by paying unavoidable costs first
➢ Set a priority to clear up all loans making you debt free
➢ Save something each month after clearing all loans
➢ A mortgage should not be viewed as a debt as it may be costing you 'nothing' compared to paying rent and it puts a roof over your head

A Lifestyle Business

What Makes the Difference?

As we have already discussed, a lifestyle business can be started in your spare time, using your talents to earn in addition to your day job.

If photography is your forte, for example, you could take wedding photos and receive a fee for your time. The problem here is that if you are not physically present, then you don't earn and at the end of say ten years you have nothing you can sell on. Another scenario could be to take photos and offer them through a portal to others. This would produce a 'residual income', earning even when you are not there. Creating a residual income through your lifestyle business is the key to potentially bigger earnings.

What can you create that will sell on a regular basis?

Rental property falls into this category; as do royalties from your book, eBook, invention, piece of music ...

Start working part time toward your financial freedom by creating assets that will produce a residual income. Grow the idea so you can work at it full time.

What is the Big Secret to Wealth Creation?

Live Within Your Means

Throughout this book we have spoken about lifestyle choices. Here is a lifestyle choice: You can either make your wages fit your lifestyle by earning enough to support it, or make your lifestyle fit your wages. Either way live within your means.

Save Something Every Month

What are your priorities, a midweek night out with friends or financial freedom? You don't have to save hundreds each month, small amounts add up. If you have difficulty saving, consider setting up a standing order from your current account direct to a savings account.

Invest When You Can

Your first investment should be a deposit to get you on the property ladder. If you are already a homeowner consider starting a lifestyle business. Dabbling on the stock market can also be done from home. Technology has made it easier than ever to get information about opportunities.

It's not really rocket science? There are no get rich quick schemes. The majority of well-off people got there through hard work and managing their money using the above principles.

 hotlifestyle.info/Wealth

Let's Sum Up

Carry out an audit so you know where your money is going.

If you're living above your means prioritize your spending.

Get out of debt and stay out of debt!

Why do you need a car? Don't buy emotionally.

Buying a property should be your first investment.

Understand what could create a residual income.

Learn to manage your personal finances properly.

Invest in yourself by putting money aside each month.

When you can, invest your savings wisely.

What You Can Achieve

Living a debt-free existence may help you sleep better.

Financial freedom is great motivation for making savings.

A satisfying lifestyle business that creates a residual income.

Final Thoughts on Enterprise

In this uncertain world, with non-existent job security, you should understand your strengths and weaknesses relating to the world of enterprise. Being flexible and creative about the kind of work you could enjoy will serve you better than narrowing your choices to what you know you can do today.

Pensions are diminishing, and the age of retirement is increasing. Too early for many of you to be considering these issues, I hear you say. Finances aside, niche businesses will always be successful and can be continued well past retirement age. A huge problem for retirees is often boredom, a lifestyle business not only brings in extra income, it also keeps you busy doing something you enjoy.

Financial independence is achieved by under 5% of the population. The fact is, it could be achieved by everyone, even those on fairly low incomes, if they made better choices and had a little discipline. Financial independence comes from earning enough from your assets to cover essential expenses. If you reach this position and decide to work at things that you enjoy, at times you want to work, this would give you an excess of money.

There are many reasons that make it more likely you will reach financial independence with your own business, which is why we discussed going it alone in such detail.

The 30-Day Enterprise Challenge

Find out if you are living beyond your means and try to adjust your spending this month to stay within budget.

Consider opening a savings account and make a standing order transfer of 5%-8% of your net income per month.

Take some time out and consider what kind of lifestyle business you could be engaged in if you suddenly lost your current job.

THE EPILOGUE

Our journey together has not ended here, it has just begun. People start out with good intentions and, as with New Year's resolutions, then fall by the wayside. Most people eat fast food and don't exercise. Most people overindulge on alcohol and sugar and don't sleep well. Most people choose TV and video games over learning and the pursuit of real friendships. Don't be like most people.

As we have discussed throughout this book it is the quality of your choices that define the quality of your life. It's time to break away from the distractions that bombard us and waste our time. Watching TV is simply watching other people earning a living. Eating fast food and not exercising is giving you brain fog. Once you start embracing healthy habits your world will open up and gain momentum from your new vitality. It is said that continuous learning keeps us young, so go out and learn something. Smile at someone, start a conversation, it's time to try something new.

I have adhered to the values in this book for most of my life. If you want to improve your life, then you will have to quit the mediocre. I wrote this book to help you transform your life into something amazing. It is now up to you!

Here's to your Hotlifestyle

Paul McQueen

CONTRIBUTORS

Pollyanna Hale

Pollyanna is a qualified personal trainer and weight loss coach and the author of Eat Drink and Be Slim and The Complete Diet and Lifestyle Plan for Mums. Website: thefitmumformula.com

David Rogers BA(Hons) BSc(Hons) MSc

David is a chartered physiotherapist with 25 years' experience of helping people with musculoskeletal pain to recover function and regain their quality of life. David lectures throughout the UK and is the author of Back to Life: How to Unlock Your Pathway to Recovery When Back Pain Persists, published by Random House.

Mike Bryson

Mike is one of the most experienced caricaturists in the UK. He also accepts commissions for picture books, humorous illustration work, cartoons, brochures, magazine features, visualization work, animated explainer videos, and talking caricatures. Website: drawnbymike.com

All our Books are INTERACTIVE

Free Online Bonus Material

Step 1
Scan the QR

Step 2
Watch the Videos

Hotlifestyle
Sleep Strategies

For a Good Night's Sleep Every Night.

Getting a restful night's sleep is easier than you think with proven strategies to break you out of the cycle of tiredness. Establish healthy sleep patterns in record time forming good habits, avoiding the things that hinder a good night's sleep.

www.Hotlifestyle.info/sleep

Brexit Exposed

The Brexit Chronicles

Documenting facts, explaining why Brexit was inevitable and the only option left. The British Parliament defying their voters, trying to stop Brexit from happening by any means. Probably the most important book on the subject ever to be released.

www.BrexitChronicles.co.uk

Hotlifestyle.info

 Paulmcqueen.co.uk

Printed in Great Britain
by Amazon

19033296R00169